KT-371-446

© Peter Steyn / Ardea.com

£6.99

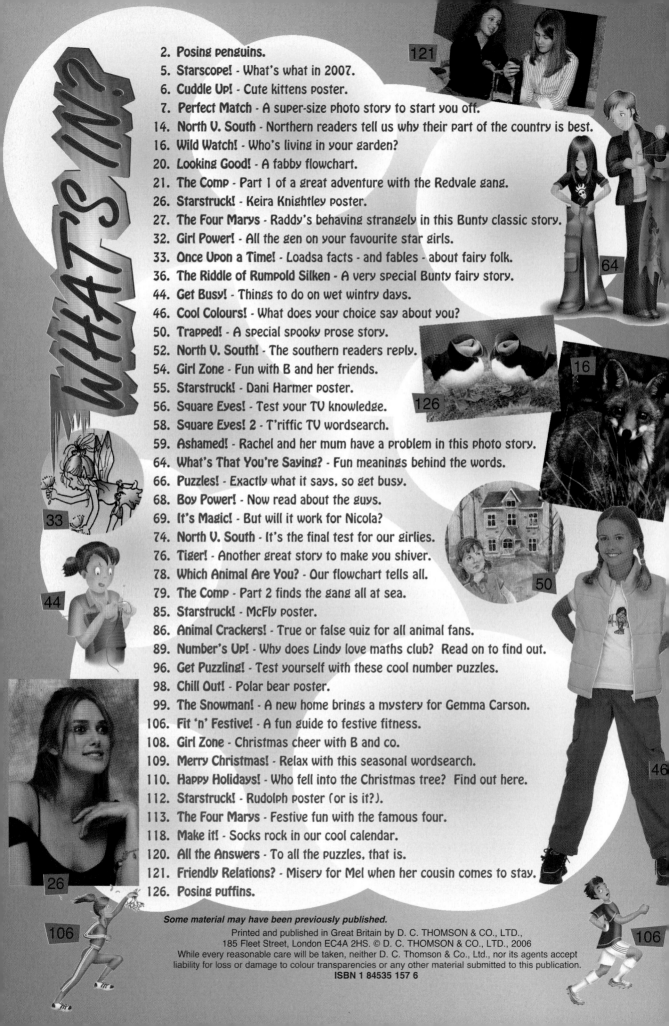

Some material may have been previously published.

Printed and published in Great Britain by D. C. THOMSON & CO., LTD., 185 Fleet Street, London EC4A 2HS. © D. C. THOMSON & CO., LTD., 2006
While every reasonable care will be taken, neither D. C. Thomson & Co., Ltd., nor its agents accept liability for loss or damage to colour transparencies or any other material submitted to this publication.
ISBN 1 84535 157 6

Starscope!

Check out your year ahead.

ARIES
March 21 - April 20
2007 should get off to a great start for girls born under this sign. An invitation in the first quarter could lead to something quite exciting and watch out for more fun arriving in your life around September.

TAURUS
April 21 - May 20
June looks like being the best month for Taurus girls - but that doesn't mean the rest of the year will be dull. A letter or phonecall from someone far away could have your whole family excited.

GEMINI
May 21 - June 20
A new friend could be set to join your crowd in the spring. Someone may not be happy about the situation, but it will all work out well. School may seem dull - but there's a welcome surprise just around the corner.

CANCER
June 21 - July 22
A special holiday could be on the cards for you this year, and it's likely to be to somewhere you've only ever dreamed about. A friend might also have a very exciting secret to share with you in April.

LEO
July 23 - August 22
Things look like being quite quiet for you - until May or June, that is. Around that time you might hear something that could mean big - but good - changes for you. There's romance ahead, too.

VIRGO
August 23 - September 22
Friendship is starred for you in 2007, so whether it's making new friends or hanging out with old ones, you'll be having fun. Major decisions should be left until November or December, when you'll be at your brightest.

LIBRA
September 23 - October 22
You could be in for a run of good luck later this year, so don't worry if things are a bit slow to begin with. A younger member of the family might spring a big surprise over the summer - so be warned.

SCORPIO
October 23 - November 22
Any worries should be cleared up before the year is very old, so don't let them get you down. An unexpected gift or money may well be on its way to you in spring - and there's news of a friend, too.

SAGITTARIUS
November 23 - December 22
A holiday could turn out to be even better than expected and lead to some exciting and lasting new friendships. You might also find yourself being centre of attention at some point during the year. Enjoy!

CAPRICORN
December 23 - January 20
Something that's been puzzling you should become quite clear before the beginning of March. There's something happening at school, too, and it could mean welcome changes for you after summer.

AQUARIUS
January 21 - February 19
Lack of money is sometimes a problem - but not in 2007. A little extra cash could mean that you will be able to treat yourself to something you've always wanted. The number seven might be lucky for you this year.

PISCES
February 20 - March 20
A tasty bit of gossip could reach your ears, but try not to spread it, or you may upset someone. A relative could come up with an exciting idea in late summer, and you may hear news of a special party or event.

CUDDLE UP!

© John Daniels / Ardea.com

10

11

THE END

North V South

Does the north rock? Is the south cool? We decided to let some girls from the two opposite ends of England tell us why they think their part of the country is best.

First meet our northern lasses, Helen, Alex, Jo and Holly. They live in the Newcastle and Gateshead area and they had *lots* to say!

what's on offer for visitors?

Loads 'n' loads! There are fabby museums and galleries, such as the Baltic Centre for Contemporary Art, and Sage, which is a great new centre for musical education and performance. Visitors should also make sure they see all the bridges. There are loads of bridges connecting Gateshead and Newcastle - including the very famous Tyne Bridge and the ultra cool Millenium Bridge. This is a footbridge and it can tilt, making it look like a blinking eye. There is also the Castle Keep. This stands on the sight of an earlier castle, which was built by William the Conqueror's son. He called it the New Castle - so that's how the city got its name.

There are several theatres in Newcastle, and visitors should visit the Theatre Royal, and try to get a backstage tour at the City Hall Theatre.

The Angel of the North is a huge statue by the side of the road leading into the city. It's very popular. There are several parks in the area, too. These include Leazes Park and Jesmond Dene, which is a narrow valley which has been laid out with waterfalls and pools. And the sea-side is just 20 minutes away by Metro.

Oh, yes, and in the last week of June every year there is The Hoppings. This is possibly Europe's largest travelling fair - and it's *great*.

The girls set out to show us the sights.

14

The famous bridges of Newcastle. The Tyne Bridge is in the distance and the Millenium Bridge is right behind us.

But what about the shops?

Newcastle and Gateshead are famous for their good shops. People travel from miles around to shop in the major centres, like Eldon Square or the MetroCentre, which is the largest indoor shopping centre in Europe. There are also lots of shops in Northumberland Street, and markets and smaller arcades in other parts of the town, too.

Bad points!

There are too many students, so they make the town very busy during term time. That's about it, really.

So which is best?

And how about days out?

Beamish, the sea-side, Hadrian's Wall, Holy Island, Alnwick Castle and loads more are all within easy reach. At Alnwick Castle, there are all sorts of great things to see and do. It also featured in some of the Harry Potter films, so you can walk in the footsteps of the stars. Beamish is really cool! It is a working, living open air museum where visitors can walk around and see what life was *really* like in this area long ago. Other great days out include trips to the coast. There are miles and miles of sea-side in the north, so you can choose between built-up holiday resorts or deserted beaches. And if it's fun you're after, then Blue Reef Aquarium, Wet 'n' Wild Waterpark, Sea Life Centre and Metroland - Europe's largest indoor fun fair - are all within easy reach.

The girls didn't have to think very hard about this question - although not all were born and bred in the north. Holly used to live in Australia, which she loves most of all, but she wouldn't swap her new home for any other spot in England.

Holly: The people here are the friendliest and we've got great shops.
Helen: We're really near the sea - *and* we've got The Hoppings!
Jo: I used to live in Lincoln, but I think Newcastle is 'canny' - which means good.
Alex: Yeah! I love the way we speak - and our special words. 'Haway' the north!

But will the girls from the south agree? Turn to page 52 and find out.

There's a good view of the Baltic Centre from here.

Time for a rest. Sight-seeing is hard work.

15

Who's Living in Your Garden?

Hedgehogs aren't just found under hedges.

You're probably all aware of the birds that visit your garden, but what about the other shy creatures that live just beyond your doorstep? Here are a few you might spot if you look closely.

A Mouse-eared bat searches for his supper.

HEDGEHOG

You're most likely to meet these prickly little fellows on a summer night, especially after a rainfall when they'll come out to search for bugs. The hedgehog has poor eyesight, but can smell and hear very well - and he's an ace climber and swimmer, too. Although he's small, his prickly spines are a great defence against his enemies. If he's scared or threatened, he just rolls himself into a spiny ball until the other animal goes away! You'll know he's about because, if you listen closely, you might be lucky enough to hear him snuffling as he searches for his fave food - earthworms, beetles, slugs and snails. Mmmm! Try putting out some cat or dog food and you may even see him feeding on your doorstep.

BAT

There are lots of different species of bat living in Britain, including Natterer's bats, Long-eared bats, Horseshoe bats and Mouse-eared bats, but the smallest and most wide spread is the Common Pipistrelle. You're most likely to spot these 'flying mice' in the early evening, when they come out to feed on moths, gnats and other small insects. Almost blind, bats use a kind of radar to help them hunt their prey and avoid flying into buildings and other obstacles. They call into the night and wait for the sound to bounce off things and come back to them. That way, they can tell just how big a thing is and how close it is.

The bat builds his home in buildings, bat boxes and trees. Like the hedgehog, he hibernates over the winter months, so you'll only see him in late spring, summer and early autumn.

© J Daniels, W Curth, B Bevan / Ardea.com

16

EUROPEAN MOLE

This round little creature has black, velvety fur and looks really sweet! His front feet are like little spades with sharp claws, while his back feet are so small as to be almost invisible. He has a pink snout, small eyes and a short furry tail.

The mole is a great digger so, if he lives in your garden, he'll leave piles of earth, called molehills, all over your lawn. In fact, as he spends most of his time underground, that is probably the *only* way you will know if he is around. His long tunnels cover a wide area and open into large sleeping and nesting chambers full of dry grass. The mole mainly eats earthworms, but also enjoys small snakes and lizards. While Mr and Mrs Mole look very cute, their tunnels can do lots of damage to gardens and crops - so not everyone is thrilled to find them on their ground.

Mr Mole seldom sees the light of day.

BROWN RAT

The brown rat has coarse brown or black fur, a pale belly and a long tail. His favourite meals include cereals, meat, fish, vegetables, weeds, earthworms, fruit and nuts. Although he prefers to hunt at night, he does sometimes come out during the day if there is food around. He's an excellent swimmer, and has a very good sense of smell and sharp hearing.

In the wild, the rat can spread disease and cause a lot of damage, but he's also clever and cute and, when domesticated, can make a very loving pet.

Ratty and his friends are real fruit and nut fans.

COMMON TOAD

Although the common toad covers himself in nasty stuff to stop other animals wanting to eat him, this doesn't deter grass snakes and hedgehogs who consider him a tasty snack! If he isn't eaten, however, he can live for up to forty years - which is a great age! His warty skin, which he sheds regularly, can be dark brown, grey, olive or sandy coloured, and he has a grey-white belly. He likes to live in damp areas and sleeps from October until March.

The toad catches insects etc on his long sticky tongue and, unlike the frog, he walks rather than hops.

Toad steps out for a walk in style!

FROG

The frog may not be the most beautiful of creatures, but many of these hopping amphibians can change colour to match their surroundings. Sometimes he's covered with dark freckles or has stripes on his sides and legs. Some funky Scottish frogs have black or red skin, and turn blue at certain times of the year! Frogs can also breathe through their skins, which allows them to hibernate under the water, hidden beneath piles of mud and dead leaves.

The frog is most likely to be found near water or marsh ground and, like the toad, catches his food on a long sticky tongue.

Continued overleaf

Who's Living in Your Garden?

Continued from previous page

VOLE

This tiny chap has grey-brown fur, a pale grey belly, small eyes and ears and a short tail. Like the mouse, he prefers to come out at night but, if he's very hungry, he may come out during the day in search of green leaves and grass – his favourite food.

The vole lives in tunnels, and leaves trails of scent to warn other voles to stay away from his land. He only lives on mainland Britain, so if you live in Ireland or any of the islands off the coast of Britain, you probably won't see this little creature at all.

A little wood mouse finds a cosy spot.

MOUSE

The two kinds of mouse most likely to be living in your garden are the wood mouse and the house mouse. The wood mouse has a dark brown back, grey belly, large ears and bulging eyes, while the house mouse is brown-grey with a slightly lighter belly, large ears and a pointed snout. Both are very cute, but very fast, so your chance of seeing one is quite low. House mice like to live near humans, but not necessarily in the house! They usually live in long tunnels under the ground. Wood mice like tunnels, too, but sometimes build their nests in tree holes! Both mice are nocturnal, so look out for them rooting in the undergrowth at night as they search for goodies.

© B Bevan / Ardea.com

SQUIRREL

The true British squirrel is the red squirrel - although most of the squirrels we now see are the bigger, stronger grey squirrels which were brought from the USA over a hundred years ago. While there is a fear that red squirrels may die out altogether, the good news is that, in some places, the two kinds of squirrels have started to live together quite happily!

Both squirrels have large, bushy tails and feed on tree shoots, flowers, nuts, fruits, roots and cereals. When there's a lot of food about, they store it below the soil or in tree hollows - although they don't always remember where they put it. The chances are, however, that when a hungry squirrel goes searching for his hidden hoard, he'll find someone's booty - leaving his own for another squirrel to find. Squirrels live in round nests called dreys and, although they look cute, they cause damage to houses and trees, which makes them unpopular with many people.

Red or grey - they're both real cuties!

Beautiful - but shy.

FOX

Mr Fox may not actually live in your garden, but he'll visit if he can! The fox is red-brown with a bushy, white-tipped tail and a white chest. He has a slender muzzle and usually has black tear-marks running from his eyes. Foxes eat insects, earthworms, fruit, berries, birds, small mammals, human scraps and eggs. They like to go out at dusk or at night and, usually, hunt alone.

Nowadays there is a growing number of 'urban' foxes in towns and cities. If you hear a strange bark at night - a bit like a dog with a bad cough - have a peek, because it might just be a fox! Be as quiet as you can, though, because foxes are quite shy and will run if they hear any noise.

FINALLY

If you are lucky enough to see any of these creatures in your garden, don't be scared - and don't try to touch them. Wild animals can live quite happily alongside humans as long as they are not disturbed or frightened. If you want to put out food for them, check first to find out what is best, and remember that milk is too rich for many small creatures to digest. If you want to give them a drink, best make it water.

Looking Good!

What's the look for you? Follow our flowchart and find out.

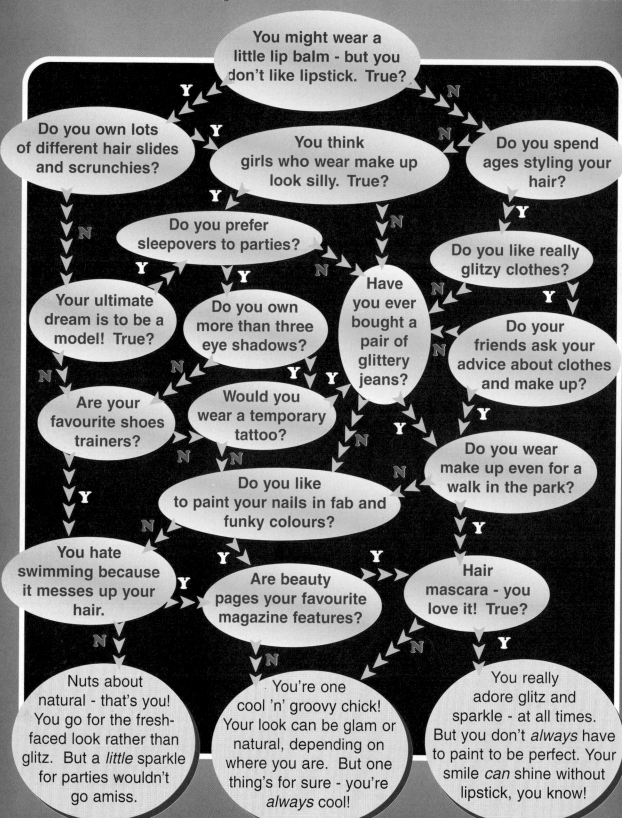

The Comp PART 1

MIND YOU, WE'LL BE EXPECTED TO DO SOME WORK WHILE WE'RE AWAY. DID YOU SEE THERE'S A PRIZE FOR THE BEST PROJECT ABOUT THE PLACES WE VISIT, LAURA?

YEAH, BECKY. NEW SOFTWARE FOR THE SCHOOL. THERE'S BOUND TO BE LOTS OF FANTASTIC BIRDS AND THINGS TO PHOTOGRAPH.

WE CAN USE MY NEW DIGITAL TO SNAP THE BIRDS, EH, HODGE. HA, HA, HA!

TCH! SILLY LITTLE BOYS. I JUST WISH WE WERE GOING SOMEWHERE WARMER. I WANT TO GET A SUN TAN.

IT *WILL* BE WARM AT THIS TIME OF YEAR, DIVVY. AND YOU'LL SOON GET BURNED IF YOU LIE OUT ON DECK TOO MUCH.

DO YOU THINK I DON'T KNOW HOW TO SUNBATHE, ROZ? I *HAVE* BEEN ABROAD BEFORE, YOU KNOW!

AND DON'T WE KNOW IT. JAYNE THE PAIN NEVER STOPS GOING ON ABOUT HER FANCY FOREIGN HOLIDAYS.

SEE YOU GUYS TOMORROW. ALTHOUGH I DOUBT IF I'LL SLEEP TONIGHT. I'M TOO EXCITED ABOUT THIS CRUISE.

ME TOO. IT'S A GREAT CHANCE TO VISIT PLACES I'VE ONLY EVER HEARD OF IN THE EUROVISION SONG CONTEST.

SO WHAT'S WITH THE LONG FACE, HAYLEY? YOU'VE HARDLY SAID A WORD — WHICH ISN'T LIKE YOU. DON'T YOU WANT TO GO ON THE CRUISE?

NO — NOT REALLY, BECKS. I — I THINK IT SOUNDS BORING!

22

OH, COME ON! I'M YOUR TWIN, REMEMBER, SO YOU CAN'T FOOL ME. I WANT THE *TRUTH*, HAYLEY. WHY DON'T YOU WANT TO GO?

BECAUSE I HATE SAILING, THAT'S WHY! DON'T YOU REMEMBER HOW SEA SICK I WAS ON THAT CHRISTMAS CRUISE? I JUST COULDN'T GO THROUGH ALL THAT AGAIN — BUT I DON'T WANT THE OTHERS TO KNOW.

OH, YEAH, I'D FORGOTTEN. BUT I WON'T SAY A WORD, HAYLEY. AND I'LL HELP YOU THINK OF A GOOD EXCUSE, SO NO ONE ELSE KNOWS THE TRUTH.

THANKS, BECKY. THAT'S A RELIEF.

So, at school next day —

AS MUM'S HAD HER HOURS CUT AT THE SUPERMARKET, ONLY ONE OF US CAN GO ON THE CRUISE. AND I WON THE DRAW.

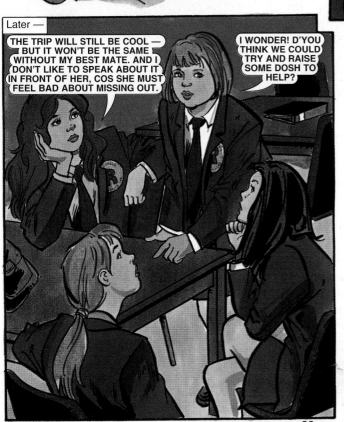

Later —

THE TRIP WILL STILL BE COOL — BUT IT WON'T BE THE SAME WITHOUT MY BEST MATE. AND I DON'T LIKE TO SPEAK ABOUT IT IN FRONT OF HER, COS SHE MUST FEEL BAD ABOUT MISSING OUT.

I WONDER! D'YOU THINK WE COULD TRY AND RAISE SOME DOSH TO HELP?

BRILLIANT IDEA, AMY. WE COULD ALL FIND ODD JOBS TO DO TO RAISE SOME CASH.

BUT WE'D BETTER NOT TELL BECKY OR SHE MIGHT BLAB TO HAYLEY.

23

So Roz walked neighbours' dogs —

HEY! STEADY ON THERE.

Amy and Claire helped with shopping —

HERE YOU ARE, MRS POTTER.

THANKS, GIRLS. NOW I'LL GIVE YOU SOMETHING FOR YOUR COLLECTION.

Laura even persuaded Hodge and Freddy to help —

COME ON, YOU LAZY LOUTS. PUT YOUR BACKS INTO IT.

PHEW! YOU'D MAKE A GREAT SLAVE-DRIVER, BRADY.

And, eventually —

WE ALL THOUGHT IT WAS ROTTEN YOU WERE GOING TO MISS OUT, HAYLEY, SO WE CLUBBED TOGETHER AND RAISED YOUR SHARE OF THE COST.

MY MUM SAYS IT'S GOOD TO HELP PEOPLE IN NEED.

WHAT?

OH, NO! I'LL HAVE TO OWN UP!

. . . SO YOU SEE, WE MADE UP THE STORY ABOUT NOT BEING ABLE TO AFFORD THE COST, COS I DIDN'T WANT YOU ALL TO KNOW THAT I WAS SCARED OF BEING SEA SICK.

WIMP!

MY MUM SAYS SEA SICKNESS IS ALL IN THE MIND. IF YOU DON'T *WANT* TO BE SICK YOU WON'T BE!

OBVIOUSLY YOUR MUM'S NEVER BEEN SEA SICK, MARGARET, OR SHE WOULDN'T SPOUT SUCH RUBBISH. AND *YOU* SHOULD JUST SHUT UP, TOO, JAYNE.

24

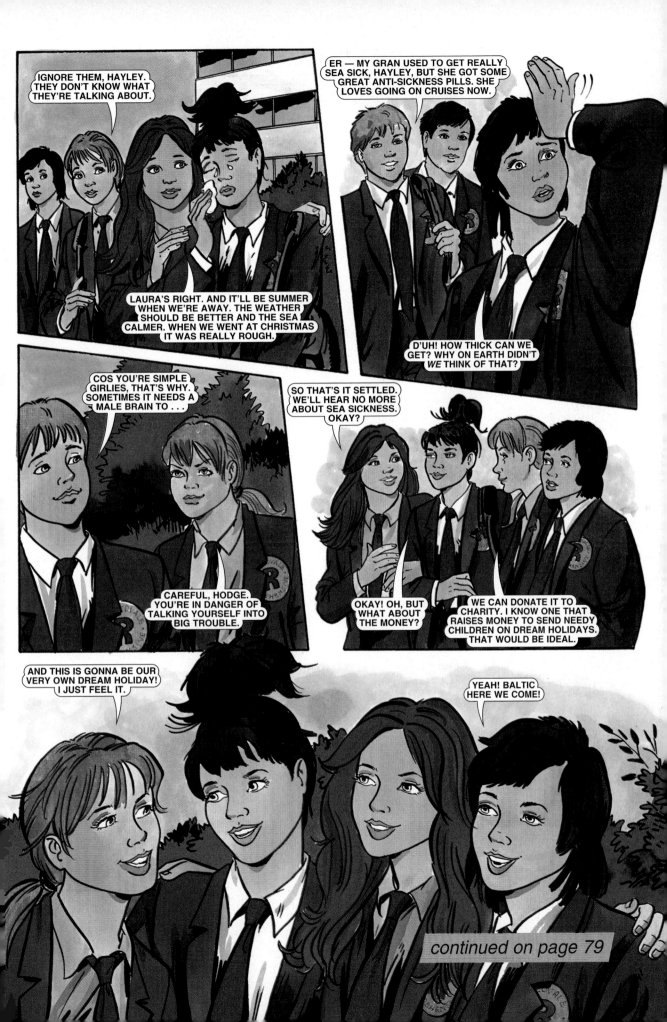

IGNORE THEM, HAYLEY. THEY DON'T KNOW WHAT THEY'RE TALKING ABOUT.

ER — MY GRAN USED TO GET REALLY SEA SICK, HAYLEY, BUT SHE GOT SOME GREAT ANTI-SICKNESS PILLS. SHE LOVES GOING ON CRUISES NOW.

LAURA'S RIGHT. AND IT'LL BE SUMMER WHEN WE'RE AWAY. THE WEATHER SHOULD BE BETTER AND THE SEA CALMER. WHEN WE WENT AT CHRISTMAS IT WAS REALLY ROUGH.

D'UH! HOW THICK CAN WE GET? WHY ON EARTH DIDN'T *WE* THINK OF THAT?

COS YOU'RE SIMPLE GIRLIES, THAT'S WHY. SOMETIMES IT NEEDS A MALE BRAIN TO . . .

SO THAT'S IT SETTLED. WE'LL HEAR NO MORE ABOUT SEA SICKNESS. OKAY?

CAREFUL, HODGE. YOU'RE IN DANGER OF TALKING YOURSELF INTO BIG TROUBLE.

OKAY! OH, BUT WHAT ABOUT THE MONEY?

WE CAN DONATE IT TO CHARITY. I KNOW ONE THAT RAISES MONEY TO SEND NEEDY CHILDREN ON DREAM HOLIDAYS. THAT WOULD BE IDEAL.

AND THIS IS GONNA BE OUR VERY OWN DREAM HOLIDAY! I JUST FEEL IT.

YEAH! BALTIC HERE WE COME!

continued on page 79

STARSTRUCK!

Keira Knightley

The Four Marys

A BUNTY CLASSIC

MARY RADLEIGH, Mary Simpson, Mary Cotter and Mary Field were good friends in the Third Form at St. Elmo's School for Girls. One day, as Mary Radleigh arrived at school for the start of the spring term —

STOP BY THE MAIN DOOR, JENKINS — AND HERE'S TEN POUNDS FOR YOUR TROUBLE.

HEY, YOU! GET SOMEONE TO COME AND CARRY MY BAGS. MARY COTTER, PERHAPS. AND MAKE IT SNAPPY.

MARY RADLEIGH HAS ARRIVED, HEADMISTRESS. AND SHE *LOOKS* PERFECTLY NORMAL.

PERHAPS, MISS CREEF. BUT HER FATHER SAYS THE SKIING ACCIDENT HAS LEFT HER A CHANGED PERSON.

AS YOU KNOW, MARY RECEIVED A BLOW TO THE HEAD AND SUFFERED SEVERE AMNESIA.

BUT HER MEMORY HAS RETURNED, HASN'T IT?

MY CD'S FINISHED. CHANGE IT, SIMPSON.

YOU COULD TRY SAYING 'PLEASE'.

DON'T TELL *ME* WHAT TO DO! IF YOU DON'T LIKE SHARING MY STUDY, ASK FOR A MOVE. I'M SURE OTHER PUPILS WILL BE QUEUING UP TO SHARE WITH AN EARL'S DAUGHTER.

I DOUBT IT! NOT IF THEY KNOW HOW SHE BEHAVES.

But two people were *very* interested in being friendly with Raddy —

LADY MARY'S COME TO HER SENSES AT LAST, MABEL. SHE'S FINALLY REALISED THOSE OTHER MARYS ARE BENEATH HER.

LET'S INVITE HER TO JOIN OUR STUDY, VERONICA.

So —

WHERE ARE YOU GOING, RADDY?

LADY MARY IS COMING TO SHARE *OUR* STUDY.

YES. MABEL AND VERONICA KNOW HOW TO TREAT A MEMBER OF THE ARISTOCRACY.

THANK YOU, LADY MARY!

The following day —

RADDY'S HARDLY SAID TWO WORDS TO US. SHE SPENDS ALL HER TIME WITH THE SNOBS NOW.

Then —

I NEED FOUR PEOPLE TO CATALOGUE SOME NEW BOOKS FOR THE LIBRARY. RADLEIGH, SIMPSON, FIELD AND COTTER CAN DO IT.

ONCE WE'D HAVE HAD FUN WORKING TOGETHER — BUT NOT ANY MORE. OH, WELL, WE'LL HAVE TO MAKE THE BEST OF IT.

THIS JOB SHOULDN'T BE TOO BAD. AT LEAST WE'LL GET TO SEE THE NEW BOOKS FIRST.

I THINK IT SOUNDS BORING, AND I CERTAINLY DON'T INTEND TO DO ANY ACTUAL WORK.

I'LL SIT HERE AND READ WHILE YOU THREE ARE BUSY.

NOW WAIT A MINUTE . . .

LEAVE IT, COTTY. IT'S NOT WORTH ARGUING.

PASS ME THAT BIG VOLUME NEXT, COTTY.

OKAY!

I HOPE YOU DON'T EXPECT ME TO MOVE.

OF COURSE NOT, MY LADY! I — OH — LOOK OUT!

AAAGH!

LADY MARY! ARE YOU OKAY?

YES, I THINK SO. BUT WHAT'S WHAT THE LADY MARY BIT? OH, DEAR . . .

. . . IT'S ALL COMING BACK TO ME NOW. I HIT MY HEAD IN A SKIING ACCIDENT, AND LOST MY MEMORY. WHEN IT STARTED TO COME BACK, I'D FORGOTTEN THE PERSON I USED TO BE. I— I'VE BEEN HORRIBLE, HAVEN'T I?

ER — YEAH! BUT FORGET IT! JUST AS LONG AS YOU'RE ALL RIGHT NOW.

DON'T WORRY — I AM!

LADY MARY! DO YOU NEED ANYTHING?

YES. I'D LIKE ALL SNOBS TO LEAVE THE ROOM, PLEASE.

WHAT?

COME ON, YOU THREE — LET'S GO TO THE STUDY FOR TEA AND BISCUITS. AND I'M MAKING IT.

YOU HEARD ME, MABEL. I'M FEELING BETTER NOW AND I REMEMBER WHO MY REAL FRIENDS ARE.

COOL!! RADDY'S BACK TO HER OLD SELF. THE FOUR MARYS ARE A TEAM AGAIN!

31

THE END

Girl Power!

They're young and talented – so here's a feast of facts on your favourite girlies

Dakota Fanning (Film actress)

Born: 23.2.94, in Conyers, Georgia USA
Real name: Hannah Dakota Fanning
Fave Movie: Gone With the Wind
Fave Actresses: Meryl Streep and Hilary Swank
Films include: Charlotte's Web, War of the Worlds, Dreamer, Hansel and Gretel
Claim to fame: Learned to read at the age of two

Michelle Wie (Sports star)

American teenage golf sensation, Michelle, was born in Honolulu, Hawaii, on October 11, 1989. She began playing golf at the age of four, and went on to win almost every junior event she entered. She doesn't like shopping much -

which is just as well, because she is either playing or practising golf most of the time. Even while at school she played for around four hours every week day, and seven hours at weekends. Michelle is an only child and her middle name is Sung.

Louisa Lytton (TV actress)

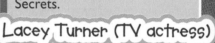

Louisa, who plays Ruby Allen, first appeared in EastEnders on March 18, 2005. She says she's a lot more sociable than her character and lists street dancing and hip-hop music amongst her favourite things. Louisa has been in several other TV programmes and actually appeared in The Bill while her screen dad, Billy Murray, was a regular in the programme. She also appeared as Hermione's double in Harry Potter and The Chamber of Secrets.

Lacey Turner (TV actress)

Lacey was born on March 28, 1988 and has played Stacey Slater in Easties since November 2004. Lacey actually auditioned to be one of the Miller family, but was given the part of Stacey instead. Lacey has blue/green eyes and grew up very near the BBC Elstree Studios. As a youngster she used to dream about being in EastEnders - so you see, dreams *can* come true.

Emma Watson (Film actress)

Born: 15.4.90, in Oxford
Full name: Emma Charlotte Duerre Watson
Best known as: Hermione Granger in the Harry Potter films
Family: Mum, Dad and younger brother, Alex
Pets: Two cats called Bubbles and Domino
Likes: Hockey and rounders
Fact: Emma is a natural blonde, but dies her hair dark to play Hermione

Once Upon A Time!

Do you believe in fairies?
Perhaps you've seen a sudden flash of light or become aware of a floral scent that no one else has noticed. Have you felt something brush against you while you were outside and put it down to an insect flying past? Well maybe – just maybe – it was a fairy.

Stories and legends of fairies have fascinated people since time began, but do they really exist? Well, the answer to that question is simple – we don't know! However, if you listen to legend, there are lots of ways in which we can raise our chances of seeing these elusive little creatures.

★Fairies are said to like music, so if you hum or sing a lot, there's a chance that you will attract some fairy folk.

★Look in the right places. Fairies are said to inhabit 'in between' places. That's places like the edge of woods or near streams.

They also like to live in trees – between the ground and the sky – or on stairs or in doorways.

★Look at the right times. Again 'in between' is best, so go fairy searching at dawn – between night and day – or twilight – between day and night.

★Be happy. Fairies are attracted to smiles, so keep smiling!

★Don't be afraid. Fairies can sense fear and will keep away.

★Have an open heart. That basically means that you should be willing to believe in the existence of fairies. Strangely enough, fairies are seldom seen by people who **don't** believe in them.

But what do you do if you are lucky enough to spot a fairy? Well, you should be very careful not to harm or insult one of the little people, as this is said to bring bad luck. And never, ever try to capture a fairy either, or you could find yourself in **big** trouble.

Now turn over for lots more fairy facts 'n' fun!

Fairy people are normally very friendly and helpful, but it's believed that some can show a destructive side when annoyed. And, because not all fairy-folk are as sweet and friendly as those pictured here, we've put together a guide to who's who in Fairy Land.

FAIRY – this is the traditional beautiful, tiny girl with wings. She mainly springs from plants and flowers. You'll find fairies attached to buttercups, roses, rowans and hawthorns – in fact, every plant, tree and shrub you can think of!

LEPRECHAUN – the name means one-shoe-maker and this Irish fairy is so-called because he is most often found cobbling a single shoe. If you see him before he sees you, you might get him to lead you to a hidden crock of gold. But, be careful! He's crafty and disappears quickly if you don't keep an eye on him.

PIXIE – the pixie has many names – *piskie*, *pigsey*, *pisgie* – and lives in Cornwall, mainly Dartmoor.

He is small, green and very mischievous – delighting in stealing horses and throwing plates in the kitchen. But he can be a hard worker, too, toiling through the night for a simple reward of bread and cheese.

UNDINE – this water fairy is known by loads of other names, depending on where she comes from – *lorelei*, *naiad, mermaid, siren, nereid* and *nymph*. She has long hair, which she grooms with shell combs, and she can be very beautiful.

GOBLIN – this little chap is usually very small, ugly and nasty. He's most likely to be a robber or thief - or even a murderer. While not all goblins are bad, it's best not to take any chances, so you should avoid him if you can.

IMP – an imp is an evil goblin who befriends wicked humans to help them in their evil deeds. Imps should *always* be avoided.

DWARF – this fairy is small, strong and old-looking – even when he's very young. He lives mainly in Germany and Scandinavia, where he mines for metal, which he then makes into magical armour and weapons.

GNOME – this fairy lives under old trees and only goes out at night. He looks like a funny old man and loves animals. He speaks their language and helps them when they are hurt or scared.

ELF – an elf is said to be quite ugly - although we don't know of anyone who has actually seen one. They have pointed ears and green tinged hair and like to roam around dark forests, where they look after the plants and trees.

BROWNIES - brownies are found in Scotland. Unlike some other little folk, they are welcomed into houses as they like to do household chores for people - always at night while the householders sleep. Brownies are invisible - so your chances of seeing one are nil! Although normally kind, brownies are easily insulted. If that happens he may turn into a boggart and cause mayhem in the household.

Now read the story of two girls whose love of fairies made them famous throughout the country.

The Cottingley Fairies

In 1916 and 1917 two cousins, Frances Griffiths and Elsie Wright, produced a number of photographs of themselves playing with fairies in Cottingley Beck, Yorkshire. The photographs caused quite a sensation, as many learned and important people, including the author Sir Arthur Conan Doyle, believed them to be genuine. Even some photographic experts were convinced by the pictures.

The girls insisted that they hadn't faked the photographs and over the years the mystery deepened.

However, in 1983, Elsie wrote a letter of confession, saying that they had drawn the fairies, then cut them out and fastened them to the ground with hatpins. Frances, however, always maintained that they had really seen fairies at the beck and that at least one of the photographs was not a fake.

True or not, the story has mystified and puzzled people for many years – and maybe the truth will never be known.

Although some of these fairy folk sound a bit scary, there's no real need to worry, cos they are very rarely - if ever - seen. It's nice to believe in good fairies, though - like fairy godmothers or the tooth fairy. So, if you ever see one of those, please let us know!

The Riddle Of Rumpold Silken

Once upon a time, in a land far away, Merrie Miller lived with her mother and father. Merrie was a pretty, talented girl, and her parents were very proud of her. One day, their new landlord, Mr Silken, and his wife called to visit —

YES, OUR SON, RUMPOLD, INVENTED A MACHINE THAT PLANTS CROPS TEN TIMES QUICKER THAN BY HAND.

AND HE'S WORKING ON A CARRIAGE THAT DOESN'T NEED HORSES. IMAGINE.

A special Bunty Fairy Story

HE SAYS HIS NEXT PROJECT WILL BE TO INVENT A FLYING MACHINE.

HE'S THE MOST HANDSOME AND POPULAR YOUNG MAN IN THE KINGDOM.

AND THE MOST BIG-HEADED, I BET. HE LOOKS BORING TO ME.

Merrie's parents had heard enough —

OUR MERRIE'S EVER SO POPULAR, TOO. ALL THE LOCAL BOYS ARE IN LOVE WITH HER.

SHE MAKES ALL HER OWN CLOTHES AND *STILL* FINDS TIME TO INVENT WONDERFUL GADGETS.

OH, NO! WHY DO THEY ALWAYS HAVE TO BOAST?

RUMPOLD READ FOUR BOOKS BEFORE LUNCH.

MERRIE *WROTE* A BOOK BEFORE BREAKFAST.

RUMPOLD CAN TAME WILD HORSES.

MERRIE CAN SPIN STRAW INTO GOLD!

WH-WHAT?

OH, NO! WHAT A SILLY THING TO SAY! WHAT ON EARTH WAS DAD THINKING ABOUT?

36

I WANT TO SEE PROOF. COME TO MY BARN TONIGHT AND SPIN ME SOME GOLD. IF YOU FAIL, YOUR FAMILY WILL BE TURNED OUT OF YOUR HOME. UNDERSTAND?

YES, SIR.

BUT IT'LL BE A WASTE OF TIME. I CAN HARDLY *SPIN*, LET ALONE SPIN STRAW INTO GOLD.

YOU STUPID MAN! HOW COULD YOU SAY SUCH A THING? NOW WE'LL LOSE OUR HOME AND . . .

DON'T PANIC, MUM. I'LL THINK OF SOMETHING.

I JUST DON'T KNOW WHAT!

That evening —

THERE'S THE STRAW AND THE SPINNING WHEEL. WE'LL BE BACK IN THE MORNING, SO GET BUSY.

YES, SIR. I — ER — I HOPE YOU'RE NOT AN EARLY RISER COS THIS COULD TAKE ME SOME TIME.

LIKE FOREVER! WHERE'S A FAIRY GODMOTHER WHEN A GIRL NEEDS ONE?

Merrie set to work, and two hours later —

WELL, I'VE MANAGED TO PRODUCE A KIND OF YARN — BUT, SOMEHOW, I DON'T THINK SPINNING STRAW INTO STRAW IS GONNA IMPRESS THE SILKINS.

BUT WAIT A MINUTE. THIS LOOKS LIKE AN OLD LOOM. I WONDER IF I COULD PUT IT TOGETHER.

Soon —

GOOD AS NEW — WELL, ALMOST. MAYBE IF I WEAVE THE SPUN STRAW INTO A CARPET THE SILKINS WILL BE HAPPY.

And —

THERE, ALMOST DONE. I JUST WISH IT LOOKED MORE LIKE GOLD.

HELLO! CAN I HELP YOU?

WHAT? OH, WHO ARE YOU?

WOW! HE GORGEOU

I'M YOUR SUPER-HERO, HERE TO SAVE THE DAY — SORT OF. NOW, WHAT ARE YOU TRYING TO DO?

Merrie explained —

NO PROBLEM! I HAPPEN TO KNOW WHERE I CAN GET SOME SPECIAL PAINT WHICH WILL MAKE THE CARPET LOOK LIKE SPANKING NEW 24 CARAT GOLD. BUT IT ISN'T CHEAP.

BUT I DON'T HAVE ANY MONEY TO PAY YOU WITH!

SORRY. NO PAY, NO PAINT! BUT — ER — I BELIEVE YOU'VE INVENTED SOME VERY INTERESTING GADGETS. HOW ABOUT TRADING WITH ONE OF THEM?

THE ONLY THING I HAVE IS MY MAGIC GAME MACHINE. I CALL IT A GAME JOY.

LOOK! YOU PRESS THESE BUTTONS AND TRY TO GET THE LITTLE FIGURES INTO THE SPACES. AND THERE ARE THREE OTHER GAMES. YOU CAN HAVE THIS IN EXCHANGE FOR THE PAINT.

COOL! IT'S A DEAL.

So —

THIS STUFF IS GREAT — BUT I WOULD HAVE APPRECIATED SOME HELP FROM MY SO-CALLED SUPER-HERO.

YEAH! GOT 'EM! KERPOW!

A few hours later —

WELL DONE, MISS MERRIE. THIS IS BEAUTIFUL — AND *AMAZING!*

A GOLD CARPET! IT'S WHAT I'VE ALWAYS DREAMED OF. I'LL BE THE ENVY OF ALL MY FRIENDS, EXCEPT . . .

... IT'LL CLASH WITH MY CURTAINS. OH, HORROR!

DON'T WORRY, MY DEAR. I'LL GET MERRIE TO SPIN YOU SOME NEW DRAPES.

BUT — BUT I CAN'T! I . . .

OH, BUT YOU *CAN,* MY DEAR. AND YOU *MUST!* TONIGHT!

THAT'S NOT FAIR. YOU'RE A ROTTEN CHEAT.

AND BESIDES, I USED ALL THE PAINT ON THE CARPET. BUT I CAN HARDLY TELL THEM THAT!

So, later —

I'LL LISTEN TO SOME TRACKS ON THE MAGIC MUSIC-MAKING MACHINE THAT I INVENTED. AND MAYBE, WITH LUCK, MY SUPER-HERO WILL TURN UP AGAIN WITH MORE PAINT.

Sure enough —

HELLO AGAIN, MERRIE. I THOUGHT YOU'D BE HERE, SO I BROUGHT ALONG SOME PAINT.

I'VE NOTHING TO PAY YOU WITH, THOUGH. MY POCKET MONEY DOESN'T COME THROUGH TILL THE 1ST OF THE MONTH.

I DON'T WANT MONEY, I WANT ANOTHER OF YOUR WONDERFUL GADGETS. WHAT WAS THAT YOU TOOK FROM YOUR EARS AS I CAME IN?

IT'S MY MAGIC MUSIC-MAKING MACHINE. I CALL IT A pPOD. BUT I WANT TO KEEP IT.

TOUGH! EITHER GIVE ME THE pPOD OR YOU AND YOUR FAMILY WILL BE HOMELESS.

HUH! SOME SUPER-HERO HE IS. HE MAY BE GOOD-LOOKING, BUT HE'S NOT MUCH OF A GENTLEMAN. AND HE'S NOT MUCH OF A SINGER, EITHER. I WISH I HAD SPARE FINGERS TO STICK IN MY EARS.

'IT'S A KINDA MAGIC . . .'

And, in the morning —

THERE YOU ARE, MRS S. TWO SETS OF CURTAINS AS ORDERED — PLUS A TABLECLOTH, SIX NAPKINS, FOUR CUSHION COVERS AND A FRINGED PONCHO FOR GOOD LUCK.

HOW WONDERFUL! THANK YOU, MY DEAR.

YOUR FAMILY IS SAFE NOW. YOU CAN LIVE IN YOUR HOME FOR AS LONG AS YOU LIKE.

JUST AS WELL, COS MY MAGIC'S TOTALLY WORN OUT. SEE YOU, FOLKS.

IT'S LOVELY, MY DEAR. A BIT ON THE BRIGHT SIDE, BUT LOVELY.

HOLD ON A MINUTE, MISS MERRIE. I BELIEVE YOU USED MY PAINT TO MAKE MORE THAN WE BARGAINED. THAT MEANS YOU OWE ME.

I HOPE YOU DON'T WANT MORE GADGETS, COS I ONLY HAVE MY MAGIC MOVING PICTURE MACHINE — AND IT WON'T BE FINISHED FOR THREE DAYS.

TOO BAD. IF, BY THAT TIME, YOU CAN'T GUESS MY NAME, THEN I WANT THE MAGIC MOVING PICTURE MACHINE.

OOOOH! YOU — YOU ROTTER! I'LL GET YOU FOR THIS. JUST SEE IF I DON'T.

NOW THIS SHOULD BE EASY. HE SEEMS TO THINK HE'S LIKE SOME SUPER-STAR, SO I'LL START WITH SOME LIKELY NAMES.

So —

. . .JUDE LAW, ORLANDO BLOOM, BRAD PITT, JOHNNY DEPP . . .

NO, NO, NO, NO. NICE NAMES, BUT NO.

Next day Merrie tried some more ordinary names —

. . .JAMES, ALAN, DAVID, IAN . . .

NO, NO, NO AND NO! THANK GOODNESS.

THIS IS USELESS. I'VE TRIED ALL THE NAMES I CAN THINK OF, WITHOUT SUCCESS. IF I DON'T GET IT RIGHT TODAY HE'LL . . . OH, WHAT'S THAT?

TUM, TE, TUM, TO, HAPPILY, TUM!

I'M SO HANDSOME, I'M SO COOL. BASICALLY I ROCK AND RULE! MERRIE'S PUZZLED, WHAT A SHAME! SHE WILL *NEVER* GUESS MY NAME!

HE'S RIGHT THERE. NOW, IF THIS WAS A *REAL* FAIRY STORY, HE'D HAVE GIVEN THE GAME AWAY AND *TOLD* ME HIS NAME.

But —

RUMPOLD! *RUMPOLD SILKIN!* YOU SNEAKED OUT WITHOUT MAKING YOUR BED *AGAIN*, DIDN'T YOU?

SORRY, MUMMY! I...

SO *YOU'RE* RUMPOLD SILKIN. WELL! WAIT TILL 'MUMMY' DISCOVERS WHAT YOU'VE BEEN UP TO!

Merrie was furious —

...SO IT WAS ALL A TRICK. HE HELPED ME FOOL YOU INTO THINKING I COULD SPIN STRAW INTO GOLD.

IS THIS TRUE, RUMPOLD? AND ARE THESE GADGETS YOU SAID YOU'D INVENTED REALLY HERS?

YES, BUT *OWWWWW!*

NO BUTS, YOUNG MAN. JUST WAIT TILL YOUR FATHER HEARS ABOUT THIS.

I HEARD ALREADY. AND, TO TELL THE TRUTH, I'M NOT ALL THAT SURPRISED. I NEVER THOUGHT RUMPOLD HAD THE BRAINS TO DO ALL THE THINGS HE CLAIMED TO DO. BUT I THINK IT'S TIME WE ALL SAT DOWN AND DISCUSSED WHAT'S BEEN GOING ON. FETCH YOUR PARENTS, MISS MERRIE.

HEY, THAT OTHER GUY LOOKS KINDA CUTE WHEN HE SMILES.

And —

...SO IT SEEMS THERE HAS BEEN QUITE A BIT OF LYING AND BOASTING GOING ON.

YES — AND I'M SORRY, SIR. PLEASE DON'T THROW US OUT OF OUR HOUSE.

THE END

Get Busy!

Go through your wardrobe and get rid of anything that doesn't fit or is SOOO out of fashion your gran wouldn't be seen in it.

Give yourself a manicure and then meet up with your mates to show off your new, posh nails.

Work out how old you are in days and hours. This may be a bit pointless, but it's kinda fun. And it'll improve your maths (maybe).

Make a mega card for someone's birthday or Christmas.

Write a best-selling novel – or, if that's a bit ambitious for starters, try a simple short story.

Make your bed! You'll be amazed at how much tidier your room will look after you've finished.

Go through your old toys and take those you've finished with to a charity shop. If there are any jigsaws, put them together first to make sure there are no missing pieces.

Tidy under your bed. You never know what you'll find.

Write a long letter to someone you haven't seen for ages, giving them all your news.

See how many silly faces you can pull in the mirror - then challenge someone to a competition.

Make up an original pizza topping – then test it on your mates.

Bake a cake. If it turns out well you can share it - but if it sinks a bit, keep it to yourself.

Have a long relaxing bubble bath. Bliss!

Learn the names of the fifty US States by heart. Then learn their capitals.

Throw out all your old mags. They're only gathering dust and you'll never look at them again, anyway.

Learn to knit. Start off with something simple like a scarf - for your teddy bear!

Dig out Mum's old keep-fit videos and bop around to last century's hits. It'll be a laugh - and it'll get you fit.

Make a list of all the countries you'd like to visit, then go to the library and find out as much as you can about the far-away places.

Open a dictionary and learn five new words - then use them in conversation. That'll impress your family and friends.

Dig out an old tape recorder and record spooky sound effects. Then invite your mates round and tell ghost stories with the spooky sounds playing in the background. Guaranteed to scare!

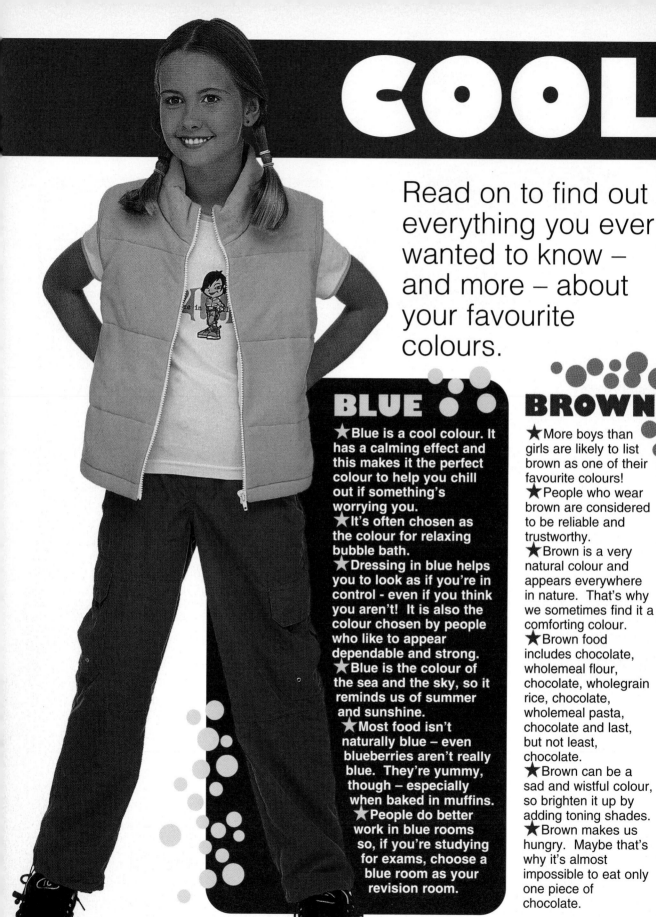

COOL

Read on to find out everything you ever wanted to know – and more – about your favourite colours.

BLUE

★ Blue is a cool colour. It has a calming effect and this makes it the perfect colour to help you chill out if something's worrying you.

★ It's often chosen as the colour for relaxing bubble bath.

★ Dressing in blue helps you to look as if you're in control - even if you think you aren't! It is also the colour chosen by people who like to appear dependable and strong.

★ Blue is the colour of the sea and the sky, so it reminds us of summer and sunshine.

★ Most food isn't naturally blue – even blueberries aren't really blue. They're yummy, though – especially when baked in muffins.

★ People do better work in blue rooms so, if you're studying for exams, choose a blue room as your revision room.

BROWN

★ More boys than girls are likely to list brown as one of their favourite colours!

★ People who wear brown are considered to be reliable and trustworthy.

★ Brown is a very natural colour and appears everywhere in nature. That's why we sometimes find it a comforting colour.

★ Brown food includes chocolate, wholemeal flour, chocolate, wholegrain rice, chocolate, wholemeal pasta, chocolate and last, but not least, chocolate.

★ Brown can be a sad and wistful colour, so brighten it up by adding toning shades.

★ Brown makes us hungry. Maybe that's why it's almost impossible to eat only one piece of chocolate.

COLOURS!

RED

★Red is associated with fire and people who wear red are usually full of get up and go and often like to be in control.

★If you're worried about a date or party, wearing red could give you confidence.

★Red is a warm colour that goes with lots of other shades.

★Even if red is your very, very favourite colour, a completely red bedroom could be overpowering. Try painting one wall red or add lots of red accessories to a pale room.

★Red food includes tomatoes, apples, peppers, strawberries and cherries.

★If you work or study in a red room or area, you'll work faster than usual - but you are also likely to make more mistakes.

YELLOW

★Yellow is the colour of the sun and brightens everyone's mood. If you choose yellow clothes, it will keep everyone around you cheerful.

★Sunshine fills us full of natural energy - so yellow is often used as a 'wake-up' colour for toiletries such as shower gel.

★Healthy and tasty yellow foods include peppers, sweetcorn, bananas, grapefruit and lemons.

★Yellow was the colour worn for weddings in ancient Rome.

★Temper tantrums are more likely in yellow rooms, and babies cry more if they are surrounded by yellow.

★Yellow is said to encourage good concentration, so many official documents and things like legal pads are coloured yellow.

PURPLE

★Purple has a mystical air about it, and is sometimes associated with magic or the occult.

★It is the perfect colour for arty, dramatic types, so you should wear a touch of purple if you are creating an artistic or literary masterpiece.

★If you want to make new friends, then wearing purple could help as it is seen as an attractive and friendly colour.

★A touch of purple, especially lavender, in your room will add a relaxing atmosphere. It will also clear your mind and have a calming effect.

★Want exciting dreams? Sleep with something purple under your pillow and you could wake up full of new ideas.

★Purple signifies wealth and sophistication and it is often considered a regal colour.

47

WHITE

★ In winter, white is the colour of snow while, in summer, it's the colour of the fluffy clouds. White is also used as the colour of ghosts.

★ White goes with everything. If you dress entirely in white people will find it easy to confide in you.

★ A white room will be very relaxing – but be prepared, cos it'll get dirty very quickly.

★ We think of white as the traditional colour for wedding dresses, but in some parts of the world, it is the colour of mourning and funerals.

★ White is a 'good' colour. A white knight is always more of a hero than a black knight and, in the old cowboy films, the guy with the white hat was always the goodie.

★ White is the colour of cleanliness. Doctors and nurses wear white to imply sterility.

ORANGE

★ Wow! Girls who like wearing orange could never be described as shrinking violets. Bright and bold – that's both the colour and the people who wear it.

★ It occurs naturally in loads of healthy foods – and unnaturally in lots of yummy sweets and cakes.

★ Orange is a creative colour and is very popular with artists. It is also a colour that stimulates the brain and makes people think.

★ Orange is a great 'cheer up' colour so, if you're feeling a bit down, try popping on an orange top.

★ Orange is said to raise energy levels.

★ Orange conjures up images of autumn leaves, pumpkins and Hallowe'en, so it is seen as an autumnal, or bridge colour.

BLACK

★ Some people may think it's gloomy but like white, black goes with everything. Every fashion season some colour is labelled 'the new black'. But black itself never goes away.

★ Don't listen to the so-called experts who say you should never mix black with other colours. We say go ahead! Black on its own can be overpowering, especially on young people, so mix it with something bright or pastel for best effect.

★ It's the colour of the night, associated with witches and wizards.

★ People who dress in black sometimes appear unapproachable and unfriendly.

★ Shy people often choose black as their favourite colour.

★ Black is the colour of authority and power, which is maybe why some teachers wear black gowns.

PINK

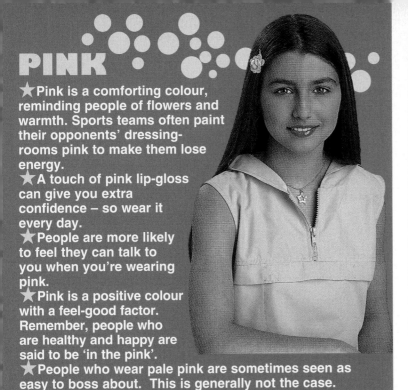

★ Pink is a comforting colour, reminding people of flowers and warmth. Sports teams often paint their opponents' dressing-rooms pink to make them lose energy.

★ A touch of pink lip-gloss can give you extra confidence – so wear it every day.

★ People are more likely to feel they can talk to you when you're wearing pink.

★ Pink is a positive colour with a feel-good factor. Remember, people who are healthy and happy are said to be 'in the pink'.

★ People who wear pale pink are sometimes seen as easy to boss about. This is generally not the case.

★ Pink is thought of as being a girlie colour but, before the 1920s, it was very popular with boys.

GREEN

★ You'll find green everywhere in nature and, as it is a soothing colour, having plants inside will help you to chill out.

★ People will find it hard to argue with you if you're wearing green! And apple green will really make you stand out.

★ We are always being told to eat our greens, because food such as broccoli, peppers, peas, courgettes, spinach and lettuce are very healthy.

★ It's said that wearing green can boost your brainpower and give you inspiration.

★ Ever wondered why surgeons wear green? It's to make the patients feel calm.

★ People waiting to appear on television or go on stage in theatres, traditionally wait in a 'green room' to help them relax.

Now choose your favourite colour and discover what it says about YOU!

BROWN
You may appear to be quiet and a bit withdrawn - but your close friends know just how much fun you really are.

PURPLE
You're a bit of an individual and like to be a leader, rather than a follower. You're great at keeping secrets, though.

BLACK
You appear to be full of confidence, but you're secretly a bit shy. You share secrets with no one but your very closest friend.

RED
You like to be noticed and are not afraid of speaking out. Keeping your temper can be a problem at times, though.

WHITE
You're happiest in the background. You love being with your mates, but you don't have to be the leader to have fun.

PINK
You tend to be a bit shy until you get to know people. Once you relax, however, you're a real fun-loving girlie.

BLUE
You make a good friend and, because you are calm and in control, you're a great person to have around in an emergency.

YELLOW
You're a real little ray of sunshine, aren't you? You probably have lots of friends and love going around in a crowd.

ORANGE
You're probably quite clever and artistic. You have a wide range of hobbies - from playing sport to watching TV.

GREEN
You love the outdoor life and are probably keen on sport. You have loads of energy and hate sitting around doing nothing.

TRAPPED!

"HOW much longer?" asked Laura. "I'm tired of sitting in the car."

"Me, too," moaned her younger sister, Clare. "Can we stop soon?" Laura and Clare and their parents were on their way to a camping holiday on the south coast of France. The Jackson family had intended to do the journey in one day, but road works and ferry delays had held them up. Now they had decided to find some place to stay overnight.

"Nothing too grand," reminded Dad. "Just a small family place will be nice."

★ ★ ★ ★

"What about that?" Laura shouted as they crawled along a narrow country road ten minutes later. "It's even got an English name. 'Hotel Poplars'." Sure enough, there at the end of a tree-lined drive was a large hotel sign in French and beneath, a smaller, rather tatty-looking wooden sign in English.

As they drew to a stop outside the house, a movement drew Laura's eye upwards. There, at the first floor window, she saw the hazy faces of a family. Two girls and a man and a woman. She smiled to herself. It looked like they weren't the only guests staying over.

Inside, the family met the owners, Mr and Mrs Gray, and their daughters, Linda

and Julie. They had come out from England several years before to run their hotel — which they said was very popular with passing British trade.

"That's why we have two signs," Mrs Gray explained. "We find it attracts British people."

"I'm glad you stopped," grinned Julie. "If you want, we can meet up later and play cards or something."

"How nice and welcoming," Dad said, when they were alone later. "And the rooms are really nice — although a bit old-fashioned."

Later, after dinner, Clare and Laura spent half an hour playing snap with Linda and Julie, before heading upstairs to bed.

As she lay awake, Laura thought about the figures she had seen earlier. She hadn't noticed any other guests in the hotel, so she decided it must have been the Grays.

"I'll ask in the morning," she said to herself as she turned over and fell into a deep, dreamless sleep.

But next morning everything seemed so rushed that Laura forgot all about the figures. All the Grays were sad to see them go.

"I wish you'd stay longer," said Julie, sadly. "Lots of people come here for a night, but it's been ages since anyone actually stayed on."

"We would work out a special rate," suggested Mrs Gray. "Even for just a few days." Mum looked tempted, but Dad shook his head.

"We've already paid for the camp site," he said. "And it's really a beach holiday we want."

As they drove off Laura looked back. The Gray family stood at the front door while, up above, the vague hazy faces of another family looked longingly down on the retreating car.

"So there were other guests," she thought. "Well, they weren't very friendly."

The holiday was even better than Laura and Clare had hoped. Every day they were on the beach or at a water park, and they made loads of new friends. No one gave 'Hotel Poplars' another thought — until they started their journey home.

Illustration by Dale Simpson

a special story
by **Katie Higgins**

"Are we going to stay at 'Hotel Poplars' again?" asked Clare as they headed north on the motorway.

"No," said Dad. "We're booked on the ferry tonight."

"But we could have lunch in the village and call on the Grays for half an hour," suggested Mum.

"Oh, let's," pleaded Clare. "I'd love to see Linda and Julie again."

Soon after, Dad turned the car on to the country road and, after a delicious lunch, they decided to ask the quickest way to the hotel.

The waiter looked puzzled. "There is no hotel of that name in this village," he said.

"Of course there is," argued Mum. "We stayed there on our way south." The waiter grew pale.

"But — but you couldn't have." He stammered. "It-it's been empty for the last twenty years. Since a fire destroyed the extension."

"And the family who lived there. What happened to them?" Dad asked.

"They — they were all killed," the waiter continued. "Some say they still haunt the main building, trying to lure families inside. It's said that if you stay there for twenty-four hours, you will be trapped in the building for ever."

Laura remembered the hazy faces at the window, and felt her own face go pale.

"I — I think we'd better just go straight home," said Dad as he left a large tip for the waiter. "We're obviously in the wrong village. Lots of these little places look alike."

But Laura knew that there had been no mistake. She didn't understand what had been going on, but she knew that they had had a very narrow escape.

And, a little way off, at the end of a poplar lined drive, the Gray family stood on the doorstep watching for a car to approach while, above, four ghostly shapes could be seen at the first floor window.

"If only the Jacksons would come back," sighed Mrs Gray. "What fun we could all have."

THE END.

North V South

Does the north rock? Is the south cool? We decided to let some girls from the two opposite ends of England tell us why they think their part of the country is best.

Now it's the turn of the girls from the South to tell us all about their home area. Meet Holly, Amy, Charlotte and Sarah. They all live in south west London and, as they love where they stay, they agreed to tell us a bit about it.

what's on offer for visitors?

Lots, is the easy answer to that question. Richmond Park, Hampton Court and Wimbledon, where the tennis championships are held, are all in the area, so there's something to suit all visitors or tourists. And the river is very close, too, so there's lots of lovely walks and boat trips available if people want to do something relaxing.

Being so close to central London, visitors to this area can easily see all the really famous sights like Buckingham Palace, the Tower of London, Tower Bridge and Big Ben. The London Eye is great, because from there you can see almost everything for miles around.

One of our favourite places to meet is beside a local sculpture which shows a row of tumbling red telephone boxes. It's really cool.

It can be very busy in this part of the country, but with the park so close it is easy to find peace and quiet when you want it. Richmond Park is the largest open space in London and there all sorts of animals living there. People go and play football and stuff like that, but you can also go horse riding or hire a bike and cycle around.

They've got almost everything in the south - but they could do with some bigger chairs!

That looks fun! But don't fall asleep, Amy!

52

But what about the shops?

There is everything a keen shopper could want here, as they can find most of the major department stores and two large shopping centres. Being out of central London, the prices are a bit cheaper, too, but you can easily go into London if you want to hit the big shopping streets. There are also several local markets, selling everything from food to clothes. It's really got the lot.

And how about days out?

Travelling to the coast is easy by car, train or bus. There are lots of sea-side towns on the south coast and you can reach Brighton in about an hour by car. There's lots to see and do in Brighton, so it's well worth a day out.

There are good theme parks, too, because Chessington World of Adventures and Thorpe Park are quite close. They're cool! Legoland is also in the area and that's a great place to visit. If you're interested in animals, then you could try visiting Windsor Safari Park or one of the nearby zoos and, of course, there is Windsor Castle and all the major city centre sights. Hampton Court is also a great place to visit as, apart from, the Palace itself, there are lovely grounds and the famous maze. Try not to get lost though!

Bad points!

Crowds and pollution. The new shopping centre is bringing in more and more people, so it's getting more and more crowded and busy. There is a lot of traffic noise, too, and that can be annoying and unpleasant.

So which is best?

Although our girls were born and bred in the south, they all have family in the north, so wouldn't mind spending a *little* time there. All agree that they want to stay in the south, though, and here are some of their reasons why!

Amy: I like the city buzz and this area has lots of history.
Holly: There are lots of places to go and fun places to visit.
Sarah: The shops are cool and we are near the centre of London.
Charlotte: We are close to several airports, so we can travel around the world easily.

The girls' favourite meeting place.

It goes on, and on, and on, and...

Now you have heard from both sets of girls, so you can decide which you prefer. But, to make things more interesting, we decided to set the girls a little quiz, to find out which group knew most about Britain. If you want to discover how they got on, turn to page 74.

Girl Zone

ENJOYING THE FILM, B?

WELL, I WOULD, JO, IF ONLY THE COUPLE BEHIND WOULD STOP TALKING.

AND THAT WOMAN HASN'T STOPPED MUNCHING SWEETS AND CRISPS SINCE SHE CAME IN.

THAT WAS JUST A WASTE OF MONEY. I HARDLY HEARD TWO WORDS BECAUSE OF THE NOISE GOING ON ROUND ABOUT ME.

ODEON

Later that week —

FANCY GOING TO THE CINEMA AGAIN ON SATURDAY NIGHT?

NOT REALLY, JO. NOT AFTER LAST WEEK.

ACTUALLY, I WAS GOING TO ASK IF YOU'D HELP ME BABY-SIT MY TWO YOUNG COUSINS.

I DUNNO, LISA. THOSE TWINS ARE A BIT OF A HANDFUL.

OH, *PLEASE!* WE CAN RENT A DVD AND WATCH A FILM IN PEACE FOR ONCE.

YOU'VE GOT A POINT. COOL!

So, on Saturday —

WE'LL GET THEM TO BED, THEN WATCH OUR MOVIE.

AH, THIS IS THE LIFE.

OH, NO! THEY'RE JUST NOT SETTLING AT ALL. I'LL HAVE TO BRING THEM DOWNSTAIRS.

HUH! SO MUCH FOR HAVING A NICE QUIET NIGHT IN TO WATCH OUR MOVIE! I THINK THERE WAS *LESS* NOISE IN THE CINEMA.

Dani Harmer
(Tracy Beaker)

Square Eyes!

How much do you know about TV? Try our fabby fun quiz and find out.

Quiz Time!

Put the correct presenter with the correct show:

a) Anne Robinson
b) Chris Tarrant
c) Sue Barker
d) Jeremy Paxman

1. A Question of Sport
2. University Challenge
3. Weakest Link
4. Who Wants to be a Millionaire?

who's who? 1.

Real NAMES, character NAMES and programme, please. Award yourself a point for each.

name game 1.

In which top US comedy will you meet these characters?

Cartoon Capers!

Can you recognise the cartoon programmes from these descriptions?

a) He lives in a pineapple at the bottom of the sea
b) Homer, Marge and family
c) Cat and mouse adventures
d) A modern, stone-age family!
e) A snack-loving, cowardly dog
f) Angelica and the 'babies'

Place the Place!

Which well-known soap is set in which place? One point for each correct answer - except 'f'. Take two points off if you get that one wrong.

a) Erinsborough
b) Weatherfield
c) Walford
d) Chester
e) Summer Bay
f) Emmerdale

who's who? 2.

Names and programme, please.

Who Done it?

A puzzle *and* a quiz this time. If you fit the names of these classic TV detectives into the grid in the correct order, the letters in the coloured squares will spell out another famous name. What is it? One point for the name and one for each of the questions on the detectives.

Poirot   Columbo   Frost   Miss Marple   Bergerac

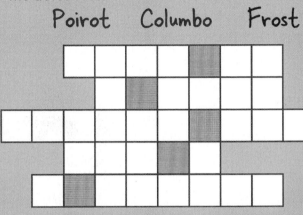

a) Who is nicknamed Jack?
b) Who lives in St Mary Mead?
c) Which detective is American?
d) Which name is also an area in France?
e) Which show was set in Oxford?
f) Which two were created by author Agatha Christie?

name game 2.

We loved him in *Friends*, but name his spin-off show.

True or False?

Simply say which of the following 'facts' are true and which are false.

a) *Little Britain* is all about America
b) *Art Attack* is a music show
c) *Big Brother* is for boys only
d) *Rugrats* is set in a carpet factory
e) *Match of the Day* is a weddings programme
f) *Doctor Who* works at *Holby City*

Answers:

Who's Who?
1. Brother and sister, Joe and Shana Swash, who play brother and sister Mickey and Demi Miller in EastEnders. 2. Louis Walsh, Sharon Osbourne and Simon Cowell from The X Factor.

The Name Game!
1. Will and Grace. 2. Joey

Quiz Time!
a) and 3. b) and 4. c) and 1. d) and 2.

Cartoon Capers!
a) SpongeBob SquarePants. b) The Simpsons. c) Tom and Jerry. d) The Flintstones. e) Scooby-Doo. f) Rugrats.

Place The Place!
a) Neighbours. b) Coronation Street. c) EastEnders. d) Hollyoaks. e) Home and Away. f) Emmerdale.

Who Done It!
The hidden name is Morse. a) Frost. b) Miss Marple. c) Columbo. d) Bergerac. e) Morse. f) Poirot and Miss Marple.

True or False!
All are false, of course. Score **no** points for getting these right, but **lose** ten if you got **any** wrong.

Now turn over and work your way through our awesome TV wordsearch.

Square Eyes! 2

Find the programmes below hidden in this mega word square. Words can read up, down, across or diagonally and letters can be used more than once.

BLUE PETER
DOCTOR WHO
FLOG IT
HOME AND AWAY
A QUESTION OF SPORT
MY FAMILY
RUGRATS
THE BILL
THE SIMPSONS

BEWITCHED
CASUALTY
EASTENDERS
HOLBY CITY
JOEY
NEIGHBOURS
SCOOBY-DOO
THE GREEN GREEN GRASS
THE VICAR OF DIBLEY

BIG BROTHER
CORONATION STREET
EMMERDALE
HOLLYOAKS
LITTLE BRITAIN
NEWSROUND
TELETUBBIES
THE NEWS
THIS MORNING

```
T W E T T A D T E Y Z B W Y S A S H
Z H V L X E H O T N E D A C Q S N C
N H E I A E L I C W J W X U O K O O
E I T G N D C E I T A L E Q O A S R
A I A E R Y R T T D O S Z L D O P O
S M W T B E C E N U T R F F Y Y M N
T S Y L I H E A M I B B W T B L I A
E H O F E R E N O M I B L H O L S T
N H E D A M B N G G E A I H O O E I
D Y X B O M O E B R U T Q E C H H O
E E D H I F I R L S E J I J S I T N
R O G T S L O L A T H E P G J N S S
S J M P L T L C Y M T J N W O L I T
U G O T H I S M O R N I N G R L N R
R R N E W S R O U N D N L K R Z F E
T S R U O B H G I E N P Z M S A X E
Y E L B I D F O R A C I V E H T S T
B L U E P E T E R R U G R A T S J S
```

Rachel's mum had great plans for her —
HOW ABOUT BEING A VET, LOVE? YOU'VE ALWAYS LOVED ANIMALS AND YOU'RE VERY GOOD AT SCIENCE.
OH, NO, MUM. I'M NOT NEARLY CLEVER ENOUGH FOR THAT.
ASHAMED!
YES, YOU ARE. YOU'VE ALWAYS BEEN IN THE TOP THREE AT SCHOOL. BUT IF YOU DON'T FANCY THAT, HOW ABOUT BEING A LAWYER?
TCH! NOW YOU'RE JUST BEING SILLY. I DON'T KNOW *ANYTHING* ABOUT LAW.
BUT YOU COULD LEARN. THAT'S WHY PEOPLE GO TO UNIVERSITY, YOU KNOW! TO LEARN!

60

62

what's That

SAY PARENTS MEAN

SAY	MEAN
I want a word with you!	You're in **BIG** trouble
You're far too young to wear make-up or go out with boys.	You're growing up too fast and you make me feel old.
It's pizza as a treat tonight.	I can't be bothered cooking.
Do you *really* need another pair of jeans?	Wouldn't you rather have a nice dress or skirt?
How do you fancy a week at your gran's?	Your mum and I want a bit of peace and quiet.
I don't care *what* your friends' parents say.	You're not going, and that's that!

TEACHERS SAY MEAN

SAY	MEAN
There's no homework tonight.	I haven't marked last night's yet.
Your essay shows promise.	But it's still awful.
Will you please pay attention?	Shut up, the lot of you!
Your writing is very individual.	I can't read this.
You all seemed to have problems with this exercise.	No one got it right.
I bet you're looking forward to the end of term?	I need my holidays – now!

You're Saying?

's a fact that people don't lways say exactly what they ean. So, to help clear up ny misunderstanding, here's ur fun guide to the meaning ehind the words.

homework

SAY YOU

I'll do the dishes later, Mum.

Of course I've done my homework!

Sue's mum says she can go.

Sorry, Dan. Mum says I'm too young to go on a date.

I like you, but just as a friend.

Congratulations! You were great in the school play.

MEAN

If I wait long enough someone else will do the chores.

Last night's, that is.

Or at least she will, if you say I can go.

I don't want to go out with you.

Push off and leave me alone. I want to ogle Steve.

But I'd have been better.

SAY FRIENDS

look awful!

Want to use my concealer?

New top?

Oh, you've had your hair done!

Of course I won't tell anyone.

Do I look fat in this?

MEAN

Tell me I look great – please!

That spot needs hiding!

Huh! That's the one I wanted!

What a mess!

Wait till the others hear about this!

Say I look fat and I'll never speak to you again.

PUZZLES!

Two pages packed with all your favourite puzzles - but no peeping!
Answers are on page 120 - but no peeping!

Word Wizard

How many words of three letters or more can you make by moving from letter to letter in our little square? You can move up, down or diagonally - but letters must be touching, and can only be used once in each word. There is one nine letter word. Can you find it? *Clue: You might do this if you succeed.*

L T E
E E A
B R C

1 - 10 *Need to try harder.*
11 - 20 *Not bad - but could do better.*
21 - 30 *Very good effort.*
Over **30** *Top of the class.*

Book Marks

Unscramble the names to discover four well-known books, then say which author wrote which story.

ABBE

KLABC UTABEY

TIMDALA

Shopping

Paris Hilton is about to hit the shops. How many of her favourite things can you find in this mini wordsearch, and which have been left out?

L I M A G S K P
E G Z P F C C E
S L F E L O I R
T I R W O H T F
E T U K W C S U
E T I J E D P M
W E T N R B I E
S R E H S U L B

★ Movie Moments

These three pictures show characters or scenes from some famous movies. Can you name the films?

THAW YKAT IDD

...oald Dahl

...usan Coolidge

...nna Sewell

...ick King-Smith

The Grand Tour

Take a trip round Europe with this cool puzzle. Starting in the shaded square, move across or down (not diagonally) to spell out the names of 10 European countries. We've given you a list of 12. Which are not in the square?

I	L	A	G	R	O	P	D
T	A	L	U	T	L	A	N
E	D	Y	E	C	N	I	F
N	M	R	E	E	A	E	N
R	A	G	Y	N	U	D	E
K	R	A	N	A	S	T	W
S	F	N	C	M	R	R	S
P	A	I	E	G	E	I	A

AUSTRIA
BELGIUM
DENMARK
FINLAND
FRANCE
GERMANY
GREECE
ITALY
NORWAY
PORTUGAL
SPAIN
SWEDEN

...ist

...usher
...ndies
...hocs
...ookies
...owers
...uit
...itter
...pstick
...ags
...ooks
...erfume
...weets

Cool Blue

The answer to every question is a shade of blue. Have fun.

1. Talc
2. Sixth colour of the rainbow
3. High voltage?
4. Corner flow (anag)
5. Flying service
6. 12pm
7. Bird with a big tail
8. Small flower
9. Not just for sailors
10. 'B a clot' if you can't unscramble this element
11. Fit for a queen
12. It's above us

Boy Power!

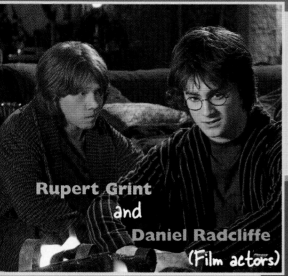

Rupert Grint and **Daniel Radcliffe** (Film actors)

Rupert, who plays Ron Weasley in the Harry Potter films, was born on August 28, 1988 in Hertfordshire and, like his character, comes from a big family. Rupert is the eldest of five and has a brother, James, and sisters called Georgina, Samantha and Charlotte. Rupert is a keen football fan and he also likes playing guitar, listening to music and watching movies - especially his favourite, Shrek. Rupert admits to having a fear of spiders - just like Ron - and his 'secret' wish is to be invisible.

Daniel Jacob Radcliffe was born in London on July 23, 1989. Although he is now famous for playing the lead role of Harry Potter, Daniel previously appeared as young David in a TV version of David Copperfield. In his spare time Daniel likes to play bass guitar to relax. He also supports Fulham FC and likes listening to punk music. His favourite films include What's Eating Gilbert Grape?, and 12 Angry Men, while his fave TV show is The Simpsons.

Charlie G Hawkins (TV actor)

Jack P Shepherd (TV actor)

Born: 14.1.88
Character: David Platt in Coronation Street
Started acting: 1999 and joined Corrie the following year
TV appearances: Where The Heart Is, This Morning, Children in Need, etc
Fave sport: Football. Supports Leeds United FC
Family: Brother, Tom, and sister, Amy
Awards: Best Young Actor in 2001

Character: Darren Miller, twin of Demi, in EastEnders
Eyes: Hazel
Lives: London
First appearance: 6.9.04
Idol: Really looks up to Nigel Harman (was Dennis Rickman in Easties) and would love to play a part like that.
Fact: Admits to having been starstruck when he first joined the cast, but now thinks filming is a laugh.

Andy Murray (Sports st...)

Andy was born in Dunblane, Scotland, on May 15, 1987, and played tennis almost as soon as he could walk. He has an older brother, Jamie, who also plays and his mother, Judy, has been involved in the game for many years. Andy shot to fame when he won the US Open Junior Men's Championship in 2004, and went on to make his mark on the senior game the following year. He learned his craft at a special tennis academy in Barcelona, Spain, and became Britain's youngest ever Davis Cup player in 2005.

It's Magic!

On the final day of Nicola Brown's holiday, she set off early to meet Mark, the boy she had met while in Cornwall –

HI, MARK! ISN'T IT PEACEFUL AT THIS TIME IN THE MORNING?

YEAH! I WISH I'D BEEN UP AS EARLY AS THIS BEFORE NOW.

NO CROWDS, NO KIDS, NO DAY-TRIPPERS. I'LL REMEMBER THIS AS THE BEST PART OF MY HOLIDAY.

HUH! I THOUGHT THAT WAS MEETING *ME*!

OH, I'LL REMEMBER YOU, TOO. I — I JUST CAN'T BELIEVE THAT WE'LL NEVER SEE EACH OTHER AGAIN AFTER TODAY.

ME NEITHER. BUT WE AGREED TO MAKE A CLEAN BREAK. PEOPLE ALWAYS SAY THEY'LL KEEP IN TOUCH — BUT HARDLY ANYONE EVER DOES.

WHAT ABOUT YOU, NICOLA?

I'M NOT BOTHERED, MUM.

WHEREVER WE GO WON'T BE A PATCH ON LAST YEAR — NOT WITHOUT MARK.

HAVE A LOOK AT THIS ONE AND SEE IF THERE'S ANYTHING YOU FANCY.

THIS PICTURE OF A QUIET BEACH REMINDS ME OF THAT LAST DAY WITH MARK. AND THAT FIGURE RIGHT DOWN BY THE SHORE . . .

. . . IT LOOKS A BIT LIKE MARK. OH, I WISH WE'D KEPT IN TOUCH!

STAPLEHAM, WHERE MARK LIVES, IS ABOUT FORTY MILES FROM HERE. IT'S A LONG WAY, BUT WE COULD HAVE MET SOMETIMES.

LETTER FOR YOU, NICOLA!

SHREDS

WHEN YOU WROTE, YOU SAID YOUR FAMILY WAS GOING TO WALES WITH SUNNYDAY TOURS THIS YEAR. WELL, SO ARE WE. SAME PLACE, SAME TIME.

ACTUALLY, I FINALLY DECIDED TO WRITE TO YOU WHEN DAD BROUGHT THE SUNNYDAY BROCHURE HOME.

YOU SEE, I SAW SOMEONE WHO LOOKED LIKE *YOU* ON THE COVER OF A BROCHURE, TOO!

THE COVER WAS A PICTURE OF A DESERTED BEACH — WELL, DESERTED EXCEPT FOR ONE FIGURE, WHICH I THOUGHT LOOKED LIKE YOU.

WHAT? REALLY?

When Nicola got home —

BUT — BUT NOW THERE SEEM TO BE *TWO* FIGURES ON THE COVER — MARK *AND* ME.

SUNNYDAY TOURS

MAYBE YOU CAN STILL GET A LITTLE HOLIDAY MAGIC — EVEN WHEN YOU'RE *NOT* ON HOLIDAY!

THE END

North V South Quiz!

It's time to see which of our teams knows most about Britain. So eyes down for our special Bunty British Quiz!

Round 1 — All about the SOUTH

1. What are The Oval and Lords?
   North: Something to do with cricket.
   South: Cricket

2. Name the river that flows through the centre of London?
   North: The Thames
   South: The Thames

3. At which sea-side town will you find the Royal Pavillion?
   North: Brighton
   South: Brighton

4. Name the large island off the south east coast of England.
   North: Isle of Wight
   South: Isle of Wight

5. Which is further south, Bristol or Oxford?
   North: Bristol
   South: Bristol

Answers

1. The Oval and Lords are cricket grounds. We would have liked a bit more information from both teams, so we've taken half a point away from each. All the other answers were correct so, after round 1, the score is

NORTH 4½   SOUTH 4½

Round 2 — All about the NORTH

1. Who plays at St James' Park?
   North: Newcastle United.
   South: Newcastle United.

2. Who or what is known as 'Rusty Rita'?
   North: The Angel of the North.
   South: The 'Angle' Statue.

3. Name the river that runs through Newcastle.
   North: The Tyne.
   South: The Tyne.

4. Which is further north, Blackpool or Scarborough?
   North: Scarborough
   South: Blackpool

5. Name the ruined Roman wall near the border of Scotland and England.
   North: Hadrian's Wall.
   South: Hadrian's Wall.

Answers

No 2 is, of course, The *Angel* of the North - not the 'angle', so half a point off SOUTH for bad spelling. In No 4 the correct answer is Scarborough - well done NORTH. All other answers were correct. After two rounds, the scores are now

NORTH 9½   SOUTH 8

Round ③ All about BRITAIN

1. Name the capital cities of Scotland, Wales, Northern Ireland and Eire. (One point for each.)
North: Edinburgh, Cardiff, Belfast and Dublin.
South: Edinburgh, Cardiff, Belfast and Dublin.

2. Names beginning with Tre, Pol and Pen are associated with a certain area of Britain. Where is it?
North: The Peak District.   South: Cornwall.

3. Five of these foods are real and one is totally made up. Spot the fake?
a) Edinburgh Rock   b) Bakewell Pudding
c) Pontefract Cake   d) Sheffield Shortcake
e) Kendal Mint Cake   f) Dover Sole
North: Dover Sole. Or maybe Sheffield Shortcake.
South: Sheffield Shortcake.

4. Which are further north, the Orkney or Shetland Islands?
North: The Shetland Islands.   South: Em - er!

5. Not counting Orkney or Shetland, name four other British islands. (One point for each.)
North: Isle of Wight, Isle of Man, Holy Isle and er...er...Ireland?
South: Isle of Man, Isle of Wight, Anglesea and Iona.

6. Which of the following is *not* a sea-side town?
a) St Andrew's   b) Aberystwyth
c) Galway   d) Norwich
e) Truro   f) Skegness
North: St Andrew's
South: Galway...no...Norwich...no...Galway.

Answers

Both teams knew their capital cities, but after that things went downhill. No 2 was Cornwall, so well done SOUTH. No 3 didn't fool SOUTH either, but nothing for NORTH, cos we don't allow two guesses. Sorry, but that's the rule. NORTH hit the spot in No 4, but SOUTH came up trumps by naming four islands. Ireland isn't quite right, so one mark off NORTH. No 6 fooled *everyone*. The answer is Norwich and, while SOUTH *nearly* got it right, once again there are no points for two guesses.

So, after all the questions have been answered, the almost final score is....

NORTH 17 ½   SOUTH 18

And finally....

For the last five points, we asked the teams to write a limerick about a girl from their area. It was tough, but both teams gave it a go.

NORTH
There once was a girl from up north,
Who in panto was cast as a dwarf.
Before she could start,
She lost her prize part.
That poor little girl from up north.

SOUTH
There once was a girl from down south,
Who had a rude brother called Ralf.
When he fell in a ditch,
She gave him a hitch.
But no 'thank you' came from his mouth.

It was too difficult for us to judge, so we brought in an expert and the decision was....

NORTH 4 ½   SOUTH 4

And that means the final score is...

NORTH 22   SOUTH 22
A DRAW

Well done, girls. It's been lots of fun!

AS Louise shone her light back down the dark passage, panic bubbled in her throat.

It looked as if her younger brother hadn't come back here after all — and now, to make matters worse, she was lost.

Louise and Ian had only recently moved to the area, and had been exploring on bicycles when they'd found the entrance to the disused mine.

"This is the mine Pete from the village told me about," Ian had shouted as he tugged on a piece of wood at the boarded-up opening. "His great-great grandad was killed in here when part of the mine collapsed over a hundred years ago. They say it's haunted now."

Louise had rolled her eyes in disgust.

"This is loose," shouted Ian. "Come and help, Lou."

"No way," Louise had shouted back, seriously annoyed. "It's dangerous! Let's go home!"

Ian, ignoring her, had swung hard on the piece of wood, then stumbled backwards with a yelp of joy as it came away in his hands.

"Got it! Come on!"

But Louise had already leapt off her bike, her annoyance turning to rage as her brother openly disobeyed her. Before she could stop herself, she'd smacked him hard across the back of his

Tiger!

A spooky story
by
Tracy Joy Holroyd

Illustrated by
Dale Simpson

shoulder.

"Ouch!" As Ian's eyes flooded with tears, he'd raced to his bike and, within moments, was pedalling madly up to the road.

Louise had sighed, then slowly ridden after him. But, when she'd arrived home, Ian wasn't there.

★　★　★　★

When, half an hour later, Ian still hadn't appeared, Louise had made her way back to the mine, sure that she'd find her brother there.

At first there had been sunlight, but that had sharply disappeared as she turned the first corner. Still, with her torch, she'd managed to see her way clearly until she'd reached a fork in the passageway. Then she'd chosen a new route and followed it as it twisted and turned.

She hadn't realised she was lost until she turned to retrace her steps. But now she hadn't a clue how to get back to the entrance and, on top of that, her torch was beginning to fade.

"No one knows I'm here," she thought miserably, tears beginning to run down her face in a sticky stream. "I'll die — just like Pete's great-great grandad." Then, as she heard a strange sound behind her, her stomach knotted. She swung the torch around and saw eyes glittering in the darkness. Watching her.

She opened her mouth to shriek, then gulped with relief as a huge, ginger cat came into view. It had a distinctive white star on its forehead and it purred as it came forward.

"Hello, boy," Louise whispered, reaching out and scratching the cat behind his ears. The cat purred again, then walked a short way down the passage and looked back, tail slowly waving. Excitedly, Louise got to her feet.

"Go on, boy," she urged softly. "You found your way in here, so now you can lead me out."

Sure enough, the cat confidently followed the mine's twists and turns, glancing back every so often with its strange, luminous eyes to make sure Louise was still following.

"It's almost as if he's come here just to rescue me," Louise thought.

Then, suddenly, she could smell fresh air. She was almost out!

As she stumbled from the mine, Louise heard voices and saw people approaching.

"Louise Turner?" a man's voice called.

"Yes! Yes!" Louise fell forward, tears beginning to slide down her cheeks again as a man and young boy approached her with concerned faces.

"Thank goodness!" the man cried. "Pete, get a blanket from the car!"

Louise looked for the cat. He was gone.

★　★　★　★

Fifteen minutes later, Louise was sitting by a roaring fire in a cottage near the mine. She gratefully drank a mug of hot milk while Pete's mum phoned her parents to tell them she was safe.

Pete, her brother's new friend, pulled up a stool and looked at her with solemn eyes.

"Is Ian okay?" Louise asked.

"Yes." Pete nodded. "He was with me. You didn't — didn't see anything in the mine, did you?" he continued haltingly.

"If you mean your great-great grandfather, then, no," Louise smiled. "Only a cat."

"Was — was it a ginger Tom with a five-point star on his forehead?"

"That's him," Louise grinned. "He led me out. Do you know him?" Pete moved to an old sideboard, opened a drawer and pulled out an old, faded photo.

He passed it to Louise, who smiled as she recognised her rescuer, leaning against the legs of a young man. Then, her smile faded.

"Isn't this a very old photo?" she asked.

Pete nodded. "It's of my great-great grandad and his cat, Tiger. They both died when the shaft collapsed in 1902 . . ."

THE END

Which Animal Are You?

Cool cat or loyal pup? Try our fun flowchart and discover your hidden animal self.

You love going out running, jogging or for long, long walks. True?

Do your mates think you're cool?

Have you ever been described as moody?

Do you have a large group of pals?

You enjoy working in a team. True?

Do you like to wear make up?

Are you sometimes a bit selfish?

Are you clever at school?

Do you spend lots of time with your family?

Do you hate working outside cos it makes you grubby?

Do you enjoy sport at school?

It's important to always look good. True?

Do you always put yourself before others?

Would you rather walk than travel in a car?

Do you like to be the centre of attention?

You hate feeling sweaty after sport or exercise. True?

You don't like eating meat. True?

Like a cat, you're beautiful, clever and just a little bit selfish. You're so cool everyone wants to hang out with you, and you can't help but enjoy the attention.

You're elegant and stylish – just like a horse. You always look great, even when you're straight from the sports field, and you're equally happy in a crowd or on your own.

Just like a loyal dog, you're friendly, lovable and kind, with loads of time to spare for family and friends. What a great, fun gal to have around.

continued from page 25

The Comp PART 2

THE Comp pupils had flown to Copenhagen where they were to meet up with their cruise ship —

FOLLOW ME. THE COACH IS THIS WAY. AT THE PORT WE'LL BE EMBARKING RIGHT AWAY, SO NO MESSING ABOUT, PLEASE.

TCH! WHY DID *SHE* HAVE TO COME WITH US? WITH GRIM GERTIE AROUND, IT'LL BE LIKE SCHOOL WITH JUST A CHANGE OF SCENERY.

AND I REALLY WANTED TO GET A PICTURE OF THE LITTLE MERMAID STATUE AT THE DOCKS. IT WOULD MAKE A GREAT STARTING POINT FOR OUR PROJECT.

MAYBE WE'LL BE ABLE TO BUY A POSTCARD ON THE BOAT. IT WON'T BE AS GOOD, BUT IT'LL BE BETTER THAN NOTHING.

FREDDY AND I WILL GET YOUR PHOTO, GIRLS. I KNOW WHERE THE STATUE IS AND, BEING GUYS, WE'LL BE ABLE TO RUN THERE AND BACK A LOT QUICKER THAN YOU GIRLIES COULD.

EH?

OH, YEAH? I'LL BELIEVE IT WHEN I SEE IT.

So —

I THINK YOU'RE BEING STUPID. WHAT IF YOU'RE MISSED?

WE'LL BE BACK IN PLENTY TIME. IT'S NOT FAR FROM HERE.

COVER FOR US.

But —

I KNEW THIS WAS A STUPID IDEA, HODGE. WE'RE LOST, AREN'T WE?

ER — NOT EXACTLY, MATE. I KNOW WE'RE IN COPENHAGEN — AND THE STATUE'S HERE SOMEWHERE.

McFly

STARSTRUCK!

ANIMAL CRACKERS!

A quiz for animal lovers everywhere. Simply say which of the following statements are true and which are false, then turn over to see how you've scored. Enjoy!

Shh! I'm trying to sleep.

Ah, ha! Smells like my dinner's out.

1. Lions spend around 15 hours a day resting.

2. Koalas have very smelly breath!

3. A rabbit can run faster than a giraffe.

4. Aardvark means 'mud pig'.

5. Dogs can pick up a scent from half a mile away.

6. An ostrich's eye is bigger than its brain.

7. The old name for a badger is brocc.

8. Cats live longer, on average, than kangaro

9. A baby alligator is called a snapper.

10. The African eleph is the largest animal the world.

Forget the doctor, just call on me.

18. A cheetah can run at speeds of up to 70 miles per hour.

19. All penguins live in Antarctica.

20. Dogs are the most popular pets.

21. A dragonfly can fly at 36 miles per hour.

22. A zebra is black with white stripes.

23. Dolphins sleep with both eyes open.

24. Baboons are the largest members of the ape family.

25. All zebras have the same markings.

26. The world's largest frog is the giant frog.

27. Dogs can be left 'handed'.

28. In New Zealand, there are more sheep than people.

29. Kangaroos are only 3 inches long at birth.

30. The largest bird is the ostrich.

11. Donkeys' milk was once used as medicine.

12. Camels are found living wild in Australia.

13. Originally penguins could fly.

14. Spiny anteaters are found all over Europe.

15. There are over 50 different species of kangaroo.

16. Dromedary camels have two humps.

17. Giraffes can lick their own ears.

Hands up if you think we're the biggest.

Here's 'licking' at you, kid!

Can you tell us apart?

87

ANIMAL CRACKERS!

HOT OR NOT!

Now check out your answers and see what they say about you!

1. False. Lazy old lions spend around *20 hours* a day doing nothing. **2.** True. Koalas eat lots of pongy eucalyptis leaves which make their breath stink. **3.** True - at least over short distances. **4.** False. Aardvark means '*earth pig*'. **5.** True. **6.** True. **7.** True. **8.** True. **9.** False. A baby alligator is a hatchling. **10.** False. The blue whale is larger than the elephant. **11.** True. **12.** True. In fact, Australia is now the *only* place in the world where camels roam wild. **13.** True. **14.** False. Spiny anteaters are only found in Australia, Tasmania and New Guinea. **15.** True. **16.** False. Dromedaries have one hump and Bactrian camels have two humps. **17.** True. They have 21 inch long tongues. **18.** True. They're real sprinters. **19.** False. Some live as far north as the equator and the Galapagos Islands. **20.** False. Cats are more popular pets than dogs. **21.** True. **22.** False. Zebras are white with black stripes. **23.** False. But, strangely, they do sleep with *one* eye open. **24.** False. Baboons are the largest of the *monkey* family. **25.** False. Every zebra is different. **26.** False. The largest frog is the Goliath frog. **27.** True. **28.** True. **29.** False, they are only *one* inch long. **30.** True.

12 and under

Wild life programmes are probably *not* your favourites. You love your pet (if you have one) but you could never be called mad about animals. Pop stars, sports stars and TV stars are the posters you choose for your walls, and zoos or safari parks probably come very low down your list of fave places to visit on a special day out.

13 - 23

You like animals loads, but are mainly interested in one or two species - probably the cute 'n' cuddly kind. You like watching wild life TV programmes, but only if they don't clash with your favourite soaps or sit-coms. While you may boast a collection of cuddly animal toys, it's a mix of pop and animal posters that decorate your walls and books.

24 and over

Wow! You are an animal expert 1st class. Not only do you watch all the animal programmes you can find, but you probably record them to watch over and over again. But while you love animals loads, you're not silly and soppy about them. Your knowledge and down-to-earth approach mean you could make a great vet or animal nurse.

NUMBER'S UP!

FOR Lindy Fowler, Tuesday was the best day of the week —

DOUBLE MATHS THIS MORNING AND MATHS CLUB AT LUNCHTIME. WHAT MORE COULD A GIRL WANT?

Lindy loved anything to do with numbers —

WILL YOU PUT THAT PUZZLE AWAY AND EAT YOUR BREAKFAST, LINDY? YOU'LL BE LATE IF YOU DON'T.

IN A MOMENT, MUM. I'M JUST ABOUT FINISHED.

But, ten minutes later —

OH, NO! MISSED THE BUS — AGAIN. LOOKS LIKE I'LL HAVE TO RUN.

Get Puzzling!

Two packed pages of number puzzles to keep you busy.
Answers are on page 120 - but no cheating.

Simply Sums!

This looks much more difficult than it is - honestly. All you have to do is use addition, subtraction, multiplication or division to work out the sums, then fit the answers into the grid. Simple!

Across
1. 51 + 51 =
3. 130 - 3 =
5. 8 x 3 + 2 =
6. 150 x 2 + 11 =
8. 11 x 4 =
9. 66 ÷ 2 - 1 =
11. 50 x 6 - 5 =
13. 10 + 5 =
14. 150 - 25 + 5 =
15. 100 x 2 =
16. 120 ÷ 2 =
17. 200 + 20 + 2 =
19. 50 + 22 - 4 =
20. 100 - 1 =
22. 400 ÷ 2 + 3 =
24. 27 x 2 - 2 =
25. 104 x 4 =
26. 11 x 10 - 10 =

Down
1. 9 + 7 =
2. 6 x 4 - 1 =
3. 33 ÷ 3 =
4. 60 + 20 - 6 =
7. 101 + 70 - 2 =
10. 100 x 2 + 10 =
11. 50 + 51 x 2 =
12. 100 x 5 + 22 =
13. 98 + 9 - 1 =
18. 65 x 4 =
21. 30 x 3 + 4 =
22. 60 ÷ 2 - 4 =
23. 16 + 15 =
24. 80 ÷ 2 + 10 =

Go Seek!

The answer to each question is a number. Solve the puzzles, then find the numbers in our mini word search. Words can read up, down, across or diagonally and each letter can be used more than once. When you have finished, the unused letters will spell out the name of a well-known book - with a number in its title.

T	O	O	N	N	E	Y	H	Y
W	N	U	N	I	T	D	F	T
E	E	R	E	X	N	E	I	R
L	V	D	I	F	A	E	F	O
V	E	S	G	T	O	W	T	F
E	L	N	H	D	O	U	Y	Y
N	E	R	T	E	D	A	R	L
M	E	N	E	V	E	S	A	T
E	F	I	V	E	I	A	N	S

a) Legs on an octopus.   ....
b) Colours in a rainbow.   ....
c) Number of Marys.   ....
d) Fingers on a hand.   ....
e) Degrees in a right angle.   ....
f) Minutes in an hour.   ....
g) Sides of a triangle.   ....
h) A dozen.   ....
i) Ali Baba's thieves.   ....
j) Top number in the charts.   ....
k) A pair.   ....
l) Players in a football team.   ....
m) Half a century.   ....

All Square!

The numbers 1 to 9 are each used only once in puzzle a and once in puzzle b. We've filled in a few to get you started, but now you have to fit the remainder into the spaces so that by adding, subtracting, multiplying or dividing as shown, each individual 'sum' totals the number in the purple square.

a

3	+		+		=13
x		−		+	
6	x	4	−		=17
−		x		+	
	−		x	8	=24
‖ 13		‖ 10		‖ 16	

b

	x	3	+	5	=26
+		−		+	
	÷	2	+		=11
+		+		+	
9	−		−	1	=4
‖ 22		‖ 5		‖ 14	

Missing Link!

What are the missing links in each of these number ladders?

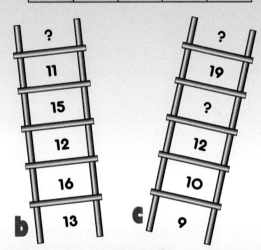

a
32
?
8
4
2

b
?
11
15
12
16
13

c
?
19
?
12
10
9

Add 'Em Up!

Fill in the missing numbers so that each row, both across and down, adds up to 20. It's fun! Missing numbers are 1 2 2 3 7 7 8 8.

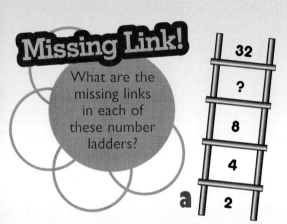

5			5	=20
4		6		=20
4			6	=20
	3	9		=20
‖ 20	‖ 20	‖ 20	‖ 20	

Number Fun!

A quick quiz to finish. We've given you the numbers, so this time we want you to supply the words to complete the phrases. e.g. **3 m-- in a b-a-** would be **3 men in a boat**. We've given you a few letters to help you out, but now it's up to you. Enjoy!

a) 5 g-l- r--g-
b) 7 d-y- in a w---
c) 24 h-u-- in a d--
d) 3 b---d m-c-
e) 2 w---l- on a b-c--l-
f) 10 g---- b-tt---
g) 365 d--- in a y-a-
h) 12 s-g-- of the z-d---
i) 8 s-d-s on an o-ta---
j) 100 p--c- in a p--n-

CHILL OUT!

© M Watson / Ardea.com

The Snowman!

GEMMA CARSON and her family were moving to their new home, just in time for Christmas —

CAN YOU HELP ME CARRY MY DOLL'S HOUSE, GEMMA?

YEAH! OF COURSE I CAN, CARLY!

CARLY AND DARREN ARE DEAD EXCITED — AND SO AM I. IT'S TAKEN AGES TO GET THE OLD FARMHOUSE MODERNISED, BUT IT'S LOOKING GREAT NOW.

MUM, CAN WE HAVE A REALLY BIG CHRISTMAS TREE THIS YEAR?

YES! IT'LL LOOK GREAT IN THAT CORNER NEAR THE FIRE.

OUR FIRST CHRISTMAS IN OUR NEW HOME! IT'S GOING TO BE BRILLIANT.

Early next morning —

HEY — IT'S BEEN SNOWING! BRILL!

THE SNOW'S REALLY DEEP, GEMMA. WE CAN MAKE A SNOWMAN IN THE GARDEN AFTER BREAKFAST, CAN'T WE?

YEAH! OH, THIS IS PERFECT!

LET'S MAKE A HUGE SNOWMAN, THEN IT'LL LAST *ALL* CHRISTMAS.

OKAY!

WE DIDN'T HAVE A GARDEN BEFORE, SO WE COULDN'T DO THIS.

HE'S THE BEST SNOWMAN EVER!

WE'LL HAVE TO GIVE HIM A FACE, THOUGH. I'LL GET A CARROT FOR HIS NOSE.

AND WE CAN USE STONES FOR HIS EYES AND MOUTH. HE'S GOING TO LOOK GREAT!

MAKE HIM SMILE, GEMMA. WE WANT A HAPPY SNOWMAN.

THERE! HOW'S THAT? HE'S SMILING NOW.

I'VE GOT DAD'S SCARF! WE CAN USE I FOR OUR SNOWMAN!

GREAT! AND THERE'S AN OLD CAP IN THAT SHED AT THE BOTTOM OF THE GARDEN. I SAW IT WHEN I WAS HAVING A LOOK ROUND.

THIS MUST HAVE BELONGED TO WHOEVER LIVED HERE BEFORE. IT'LL BE JUST RIGHT FOR OUR SNOWMAN.

HOW'S THAT? IS IT OKAY?

YEAH, THAT'S EXCELLENT!

TEA'S READY!

COME ON, GEMMA!

That night —

TODAY'S BEEN ONE OF THE BEST DAYS EVER. I JUST HOPE OUR SNOWMAN HASN'T MELTED BY TOMORROW!

Next morning —

IS OUR SNOWMAN STILL THERE, CARLY?

YES, BUT COME AND LOOK AT HIM. HIS FACE HAS SLIPPED AND HE LOOKS REALLY SAD AND BAD-TEMPERED.

OH, DEAR! HE DOES LOOK GRUMPY! THE SNOW MUST BE SOFT AND THAT'S WHY HIS MOUTH'S SLIPPED. BUT I'LL SOON SORT IT.

THERE, THAT'S BET . . . TCH! BE CAREFUL, DARREN.

OH!

WHAT'S WRONG, GEMMA?

ER — NOTHING, DARREN. IT'S OKAY.

THAT'S WEIRD! I'M SURE THE SNOWMAN'S FACE CHANGED JUST NOW. BUT I MUST HAVE IMAGINED IT, COS HE'S SMILING AGAIN.

COME ON, KIDS. TIME FOR TEA.

OUCH!

WHO DID THAT? OH, THERE'S NO ONE THERE.

WHO CAN HAVE THROWN THAT SNOWBALL? I KNOW IT SOUNDS CRAZY, BUT I'M SURE THERE'S SOMETHING STRANGE ABOUT THAT SNOWMAN.

Later that day —

ARE YOU THE FAMILY THAT'S MOVED INTO THE OLD FARMHOUSE IN LONGMEADOW LANE?

YES, THAT'S US.

YOU'VE CERTAINLY SMARTENED THE PLACE UP! OLD MR SUTTON, WHO LIVED THERE BEFORE, NEVER SPENT A PENNY ON IT.

HE WAS AN OLD SKINFLINT. WE ALL USED TO CALL HIM SCROOGE! HE WOULD SHOUT AND WAVE HIS STICK AT ANYONE WHO WENT NEAR, SO WE JUST LEFT HIM ALONE.

SO THE OLD MAN WHO OWNED THE HOUSE WAS GRUMPY AND BAD-TEMPERED. THAT'S WHAT OUR SNOWMAN LOOKS LIKE WHEN HIS FACE CHANGES.

OH, *HERE'S* MY SCARF! BUT JUST LOOK AT IT — IT'S SOAKED THROUGH. WHO SAID YOU CHILDREN COULD TAKE IT?

SORRY, DAD! WE DIDN'T THINK YOU WOULD MIND.

POOR SNOWMAN! NOW HE LOOKS REALLY SAD. HE'LL BE COLD WITHOUT A SCARF.

LET'S FIND ANOTHER ONE FOR HIM. MUM WILL LET US HAVE ONE OF HERS.

So —

THERE! THAT LOOKS BETTER.

OH, YES! NOW HE'LL BE WARM. MAKE HIM HAPPY AGAIN, GEMMA!

I LOVE YOU, MR SNOWMAN! YOU'RE THE BEST SNOWMAN IN THE WORLD.

THAT'S ODD. I WAS SURE HE WAS LOOKING SAD A MINUTE AGO.

Later that day —

IT'S CHRISTMAS EVE TOMORROW. I WONDER IF IT WILL SNOW AGAIN! OH! I — I DON'T BELIEVE IT!

105

FIT 'N' FESTIVE!

Follow our fun guide to keeping fit over the festive season.

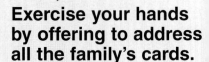

Chase the hunky school football captain with a sprig of mistletoe.

Search the house from top to bottom for hidden Christmas presents.

Offer to stir the Christmas pudding – fifty times.

Run away when the class dorks appear bearing mistletoe.

Dash to be first to the advent calendar every day.

Make up a groovy new dance routine to perform at Christmas parties.

Exercise your hands by offering to address all the family's cards.

Build up your arm muscles by pulling lots of crackers.

Hide the TV remote control so you have to get up to change channels.

Stand on your tiptoes and stretch to put up the decorations.

Deliver all your cards by hand – or walk to the third nearest post box.

Help put up decorations for the local Old People's Centre.

Peel all the potatoes for Christmas dinner.

Go out carol singing and jog between houses....

...then offer to do all the collecting.

Walk to the shops to do your shopping.

S-t-r-e-t-c-h to hang up stockings for every member of the family!

Exercise your mouth by having seconds for every course. If you've followed all our instructions, you'll deserve it.

Buy heavy presents for all your family and friends...

... then walk back home again carrying all your parcels and bags.

Have a cool Yule!

Girl Zone

THERE ARE SOME GREAT PRESENTS HERE FOR JO'S CHRISTMAS, BUT THEY'RE DEAD EXPENSIVE.

I KNOW LISA WOULD LIKE SOMETHING FROM THIS RANGE — BUT I CAN'T AFFORD IT. IN FACT, I CAN'T AFFORD CHRISTMAS, FULL STOP!

And so —

HEY! THIS LOOKS INTERESTING.

EXTRA STAFF REQUIRED FOR THE SATURDAY BEFORE CHRISTMAS

Then —

OKAY, B. I THINK YOU'LL DO JUST FINE. WE'LL SEE YOU ON SATURDAY MORNING.

WHAT EXACTLY WILL YOU BE DOING IN YOUR SATURDAY JOB, B?

OH — ER — THIS AND THAT, LISA. I EXPECT I'LL BE KEPT PRETTY BUSY!

On Saturday morning —

DO YOU FANCY GOING TO SEE SANTA IN THE SHOPPING CENTRE, YOU TWO?

visit Santa's Grotto

OOH, YES, AUNTIE LISA!

THEY'VE DONE A GOOD JOB IN HERE. IT LOOKS GREAT.

YEAH! THEY'VE EVEN GOT SANTA'S REINDEER, JO. AND THAT ONE OVER THERE LOOKS *VERY* FAMILIAR.

HA, HA, HA! IT'S B! NO WONDER SHE WOULDN'T TELL US WHAT HER SATURDAY JOB WAS.

PITY! WE COULD HAVE BROUGHT HER A CARROT FOR HER BREAK! HA, HA!

Merry Christmas!

Have some fabby festive fun with this twinkly little wordsearch. Simply find the seasonal words listed below in the wordsquare. They can read up, down, backwards, forwards or diagonally and letters can be used more than once. Oh, and to make things a bit more difficult, we've mixed up the letters, so you have to unscramble the words before you can search for them. Tee, hee!

Tip: When correctly arranged, the words are listed in alphabetical order. If you're *really* stuck, you'll find the answers on page 120.

1. DAVNET ALDENCRA
2. GELAN
3. KCEA
4. DRACS
5. LACOR RINSEGS
6. MSAHRICTS VEE
7. RACSCKER
8. RINDEN
9. SELVE
10. YIRAF
11. LOHLY
12. VYI
13. NOAMIPTME
14. REAPP SHACIN
15. RAPTISE
16. NESPERST
17. UDINGPD
18. BROBNIS
19. DRULHOP
20. TASAN ULASC
21. ESHILG SLEBL
22. NOWMASN
23. COSTINGK
24. STILEN
25. ERTE
26. RUKTEY

```
S P P S N R G S L M S E C R E
T A U C R E U N N N E Y A E V
N N D Y O E W D I O E H R N E
E T D E R U G A O K B I D N S
S O I E Y I H N R L C B S I A
E M N R D C A U I K P O I D M
R I G T R H T F S S J H T R T
P M R E S A N T A C L A U S S
L E P S R E K C A R C O U T I
A A S N O W M A N A D S R V R
P S E I T R A P A C Y E U A H
R A D N E L A C T N E V D A C
T I N S E L C I F Y G L Y A G
M V I Y L L O H V C R E K R L
S L L E B H G I E L S E L N A
```

Happy Holidays!

It's our favourite time of year, so we asked some readers to let us into their special festive secrets.

Bridget

Eleanor

Ellen

Harriet

Sophie

What's the best Christmas you've ever had?

Bridget: A few years ago I went to stay with my cousins. My grandparents were there, too, and we all got lots of presents and had loads of fun.

Eleanor: Two years ago was brilliant cos I got *everything* I had asked for!

Ellen: In 2004 all my relatives came to our house and it was cool.

Harriet: One year I got a styling head and loads and loads of clothes. I was *sooo* happy!

Sophie: We had a huge family party two years ago and I think that was my best Christmas.

What's the best or worst present you've ever received?

Eleanor: My best was a doll's house with real scale furniture inside

Sophie: I once got a green spotted dinosaur! I guess that was about the worst.

Harriet: I got my room decorated and I love it!

Bridget: My worst was a pink, piano-shaped case and my best was my iPod.

Ellen: Someone gave me a cress head. It was really boring - and it didn't even grow!

What's your earliest Christmas memory?

Bridget: When I was about five I fell into the Christmas tree. When Mum came into the room, all she could see was two legs.

Ellen: Wearing a horrible black velvet dress! Blee!

Sophie: My cat went missing and we found her under the tree, trying to get into the branches.

Harriet: When I was three I got a dolly's cot and I just loved it.

Eleanor: The Christmas tree fell on me when I was younger.

Who would you most like to kiss under the mistletoe?

Sophie: Brad Pitt.
Ellen: Jonny Wilkinson. Although, if it had to be someone from school, it would be.... no, I'm not telling!
Eleanor: Danny from McFly.
Bridget: Orlando Bloom.
Harriet: Chad Michael Murray.

If you could have anything at all for Christmas, what would you choose?

Harriet: A ride on Santa's sleigh.
Bridget: A personalised guitar.
Ellen: A trip to Lapland with my family and friends.
Sophie: That would be cool. And a sleigh ride, too.
Eleanor: A holiday in Italy - and a horse - and an iPod - and some games - and...

Where would be your dream place to spend Christmas?

Ellen: New York, cos if I'd forgotten to buy any presents, I'd have lots of shops to go to.
Eleanor: Italy. I'm half Italian and some of my relatives still live there.
Bridget: Central Park, New York!
Sophie: Me too. I think Central Park would be great - especially in the snow.
Harriet: My house - cos I love being with my family.

What's your favourite way to spend Christmas Eve?

Sophie: Sitting down with my family and watching a good film.
Harriet: Going to church at midnight and putting out a drink for Santa.
Ellen: Well, it's my brother's birthday, so we usually celebrate that.
Eleanor: Just finishing the present wrapping and being with my family.
Bridget: Watching a film and eating chocs.

Finally, tell us anything you don't like about Christmas!

Sophie: Brussels sprouts!
Eleanor: Turkey!
Bridget: Christmas cake!
Harriet: Tidying up the wrapping paper!
Ellen: Nothing! I love everything about Christmas!

Thanks, girls. We hope this Christmas turns out to be your best ever!

STARSTRUCK!

Rudolph?

The Four Marys

A BUNTY CLASSIC

Every Christmas the pupils at St Elmo's School for Girls held a party for the local village children. The four Marys, Simpy, Fieldy, Raddy and Cotty, always enjoyed helping with the preparations —

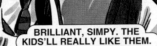

THESE ANIMAL-SHAPED BISCUIT CUTTERS ARE GREAT. LOOK AT THE RABBIT — AND THE DONKEY.

BRILLIANT, SIMPY. THE KIDS'LL REALLY LIKE THEM.

AND MR JENNINGS HAS AGREED TO BE SANTA. HE'S DECORATING HIS VAN TO MAKE IT LOOK LIKE A SLEIGH.

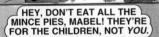

HEY, DON'T EAT ALL THE MINCE PIES, MABEL! THEY'RE FOR THE CHILDREN, NOT *YOU*.

HUH! THOSE COMMON KIDS SHOULDN'T BE ALLOWED INSIDE OUR SCHOOL. IT'S NOT RIGHT.

Later —

I LOVE CHRISTMAS. EVEN THE TV PROGRAMMES ARE GOOD AT THIS TIME OF THE YEAR.

YEAH! I'M STARTING TO GET REALLY EXCITED ABOUT THE PARTY TOMORROW, RADDY.

JUST LISTEN TO THOSE STUPID MARYS, VERONICA. THEY ACTUALLY THINK TOMORROW'S PARTY IS *EXCITING!* HUH!

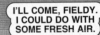

Next day —

WE STILL NEED SOME HOLLY TO FINISH OFF THE DECORATIONS. WHO WANTS TO COME WITH ME?

I'LL COME, FIELDY. I COULD DO WITH SOME FRESH AIR.

115

HELP!

POACHERS! *HELP!* MR JARVIS!

PRETENDING SOMEBODY'S THERE, ARE YOU? HUH! WE'RE NOT STUPID ENOUGH TO FALL FOR *THAT* OLD TRICK.

HE — HE CAN'T HAVE HEARD US. HE MUST BE TOO FAR AWAY.

AND THERE'S NO WAY *WE* CAN STOP THESE MEN GETTING AWAY WITH THE DEER.

But —

COME ON, TERRY. LET'S GET OUT OF HERE.

MR JARVIS! THANK GOODNESS!

OI! YOU TWO! WHAT'S GOING ON?

I KNOW THOSE TWO AND I'LL CATCH UP WITH THEM LATER. FIRST, I WANT TO GET THIS LITTLE CHAP BACK TO THE DEER PARK. YOU CAN COME ALONG AND TELL THE OWNERS HOW YOU FOUND HIM.

So —

WE'RE VERY GRATEFUL TO YOU. THANK YOU VERY MUCH, GIRLS.

ARE ALL YOUR DEER THE SAME, MRS SHERWOOD?

NO, WE HAVE SEVERAL DIFFERENT BREEDS. NOW, COME INTO THE HOUSE AND WARM UP. YOU MUST BE FROZEN.

EAT UP, GIRLS. AND, REMEMBER, IF THERE'S EVER ANYTHING WE CAN DO TO HELP YOUR SCHOOL, *PLEASE* LET US KNOW. WE REALLY *ARE* IN YOUR DEBT, YOU KNOW.

116

THE END

Make It! Cool Calendar!

We all love opening our advent calendars in December, but wouldn't it be great if we could make our own which we could use year after year? Well, now we can, cos our funky advent 'washing line' makes a calendar that can be used again and again. And the good news is that it's really simple to make.

You will need:
- *Red felt and green felt (enough to make 12 'stockings' from each)*
- *Fabric adhesive*
- *Scissors*
- *Mini pegs (available from craft or card-making shops)*
- *A length of glittery string or tinsel*
- *A pencil*
- *Fabric paint (optional)*
- *A selection of small sweets and trinkets to put inside the 'stockings'*

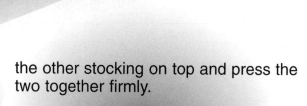

1. Trace the template on page 119 onto cardboard, then cut it out and place it on top of a double layer of felt. Draw round the template with the pencil, then cut out the felt shapes carefully.

2. Place a thin line of adhesive round the outside edge of one of the stockings as instructed on the template, then stick the other stocking on top and press the two together firmly.

3. Next, turn down the unglued flap at the top of one side, and stick in place with more adhesive. This will be the front of the stocking, leaving a single thickness flap at the back for pegging to the 'line'. This is when you can decide which direction you want your

118

stocking to point. You can either have them all facing in one direction, or chose a mixture, as we did.

4. Repeat steps 1, 2 and 3 until you have 12 red stockings and 12 green stockings. You will find that it is best to turn the template over each time, and draw all the stockings on the felt before you start cutting. That way you can make sure you have enough material.

5. Once all the stockings have been made, you can decorate them by sticking tiny, leftover scraps of contrasting felt to the tops, as in our examples.

6. To add the numbers you can either paint them on with fabric paint, or use a cocktail stick to 'write' the number shapes with adhesive and then stick thin strips of felt into place. This is quite tricky — so it might be best to practise on a scrap of material first.

TURN TOP FLAP OVER HERE AND STICK DOWN

TEMPLATE

Stockings can be made any size, but if they are bigger than this template you will need more felt.

STICK ALONG THE DOTTED LINE.

7. Once the stockings are finished and all the adhesive is completely dry, place a sweet or tiny gift inside each.

8. With the craft pegs, carefully peg each stocking to the tinsel or string in any order you like.

9. Hang your 'washing line' on the wall, across a window, or even drape it round the Christmas tree, and remove a gift every day during the build-up to Christmas. We're sure your special calendar will be well admired and, when it is empty, you can keep it in a safe place – until it's time to refill it for next year, that is!

Simple but effective. Why not make one for a friend?

All The Answers!

Cool Blue

Word Wizard

Words include:
ace, ate, arc, are, bear, beat, bee, beer, beet, belt, beret, bet, brace, bracelet, brat, car, care, cat, create, creel, ear, eat, era, lea, lee, leer, let, race, rat, rate, reel, tar, tea, tear, tee, etc. The nine letter word is **celebrate**.

The Grand Tour

```
I L A G R O P D
T A L U T L A N
E D Y E C N I F
N M R E E A E N
R A G Y N U D E
K R A N A S T W
S F N C M R R S
P A I E G E I A
```

The countries not used are **Belguim** and **Norway.**

Movie Moments

a) E T
b) Charlie and the Chocolate Factory
c) The Chronicles of Narnia: The Lion, the Witch and the Wardrobe

Shopping List

Candies and **books** are missing from the wordsearch.

Book Marks

BABE by Dick King-Smith
BLACK BEAUTY by Anna Sewell
MATILDA by Roald Dahl
WHAT KATY DID by Susan Coolidge

Simply Sums!

1	0	2		1	2	7	
2 6		3 1	1		4 4	
		6				
3 2	2	9 5		1 5	
1 3	0	2 0	0	
6 0	2 2	2	6 8	
6			
9 9	2 0	3	5 2	
4 1	6	1 0	0	

Number Fun!

a) 5 gold rings
b) 7 days in a week
c) 24 hours in a day
d) 3 blind mice
e) 2 wheels on a bicycle
f) 10 green bottles
g) 365 days in a year
h) 12 signs of the zodiac
i) 8 sides on an octagon
j) 100 pence in a pound

Add 'Em Up!

5	8	2	5	=20
4	2	6	8	=20
4	7	3	6	=20
7	3	9	1	=20
20	20	20	20	

Merry Christmas!

page 109

1. ADVENT CALENDAR
2. ANGEL
3. CAKE
4. CARDS
5. CAROL SINGERS
6. CHRISTMAS EVE
7. CRACKERS
8. DINNER
9. ELVES
10. FAIRY
11. HOLLY
12. IVY
13. PANTOMIME
14. PAPER CHAINS
15. PARTIES
16. PRESENTS
17. PUDDING
18. RIBBONS
19. RUDOLPH
20. SANTA CLAUS
21. SLEIGH BELLS
22. SNOWMAN
23. STOCKING
24. TINSEL
25. TREE
26. TURKEY

All Square!

3	+	9	+	1	=13
x		−		+	
6	x	4	−	7	=17
−		x		+	
5	−	2	x	8	=24
13		10		16	

7	x	3	+	5	=26
+		−		+	
6	÷	2	+	8	=11
+		+		+	
9	−	4	−	1	=4
22		5		14	

Missing Link!

a) 2, 4, 8, **16**, 32. Each step is equal to the number below b) 13, 16, 12, 15, 11, **14**. The steps are, alternatively, three forward, then four back. c) 9, 10, 12, **15**, 19, 24. The steps increase by one each time.

Go Seek!

a) eight, b) seven, c) four, d) five, e) ninety, f) sixty, g) three, h) twelve, i) forty, j) one, k) two, l) eleven, m) fifty. The hidden book is 'One Hundred and One Dalmatians'.

FRIENDLY RELATIONS?

Melanie's cousin, Hannah, had come to stay for a few weeks. Although they were the same age, the cousins had never been close but, as Hannah's parents were taking time out to work out some problems in their marriage, Melanie was determined to make her cousin feel welcome.

YOU'RE WELCOME TO BORROW ANY OF THESE, HANNAH.

THANKS, MEL. THAT'S KIND OF YOU.

AND YOU CAN BORROW MY CLOTHES, TOO. ALL YOU HAVE TO DO IS ASK. OH, AND WOULD YOU MIND LEAVING THE LIGHT OFF AT NIGHT? I CAN'T SLEEP WITH IT ON.

YOU'RE LUCKY, MELANIE. IF MY MUM AND DAD SPLIT UP WE WON'T BE ABLE TO AFFORD NEW CLOTHES AND THINGS.

I'M SURE IT WON'T COME TO THAT, HANNAH. THEY'LL MAKE UP AND EVERYTHING WILL BE FINE. JUST YOU WAIT AND SEE.

I — I HOPE SO. BUT I BET THEY DON'T. I NEVER HAVE ANY LUCK.

But, a few days later, while Hannah was visiting a friend —

I WONDER WHERE I PUT THAT BELT! I WANT TO WEAR IT WHEN I MEET UP WITH LOUISE LATER.

MUM, YOU HAVEN'T SEEN MY NEW BELT RECENTLY, HAVE YOU?

NO, DARLING, I DON'T THINK SO.

122

THANK GOODNESS THIS IS ONLY FOR A COUPLE OF WEEKS. BUT I WISH I DIDN'T HAVE THE FEELING THAT HANNAH IS BEING AWKWARD ON PURPOSE. SHE HASN'T EVEN OPENED THE WINDOW.

Next morning —

THAT'S FANTASTIC NEWS. NO, NO! EVERYTHING'S GREAT HERE, HONESTLY. YES, YES, THE — ER — MONEY'S SAFE. I'LL BE IN TOUCH.

I WONDER WHAT ALL THAT WAS ABOUT!

Later, the two girls met Louise —

ARE YOU SURE HANNAH ISN'T REALLY WELL OFF? EVERY TIME I SEE HER SHE SEEMS TO BE WEARING SOMETHING NEW — LIKE THESE BOOTS.

YOU'RE RIGHT, LOU. I DON'T THINK I'VE SEEN THESE BEFORE.

So —

HEY, HANNAH! FANCY GOING FOR A COFFEE?

GREAT. LEAD THE WAY, LOUISE.

... COME TO THINK OF IT, I REALLY SHOULD BE GETTING BACK. MUM MIGHT PHONE ME.

YEAH! AND PIGS MIGHT FLY. THAT'S AN EXCUSE IF EVER I HEARD ONE.

HOW ABOUT YOU TREAT US THIS TIME, HANNAH?

I WOULD LOVE TO, LOUISE, BUT I DON'T HAVE THAT MUCH MONEY. YOU SEE, MY PARENTS ARE PROBABLY SPLITTING UP AND ...

123

Later —

I WISH YOU DIDN'T HAVE TO BRING HANNAH TO MY PARTY ON FRIDAY, MEL. THE MORE I SEE OF HER THE LESS I LIKE HER.

ME, TOO. BUT I SUPPOSE THINGS *ARE* TOUGH FOR HER. I MEAN, I'D HATE IT IF *MY* FOLKS SPLIT UP.

YOU'VE GOT A POINT. AND I DON'T SUPPOSE YOUR MUM WOULD LET YOU COME WITHOUT HER, ANYWAY.

RIGHT. BUT, WITH A BIT OF LUC WE'LL BE ABLE T IGNORE HER.

At the party —

WOW! YOU NEVER TOLD ME THAT YOU'D ASKED RICHARD DRAYTON AND HIS MATE.

IT'S MY SURPRISE. LET'S GO OVER AND TALK TO THEM.

But —

HI! RICHARD, ISN'T IT? I'M HANNAH, MELANIE'S COUSIN.

I DON'T BELIEVE IT! SHE'S MOVING IN ON RICHARD NOW — *AND* SHE'S WEARING MY TOP!

I'M STAYING WITH MEL BECAUSE MY PARENTS MIGHT BE SPLITTING UP. IT'S — IT'S SUCH A STRAIN.

TCH! SHE'S TRYING THAT STORY ON *HIM*, TOO. IF YOU ASK ME, SHE'S NOT IN THE LEAST BIT UPSET.

The party was ruined for Melanie and, when it was time for home —

I'M SICK OF YOU BORROWING THINGS WITHOUT ASKING, HANNA AND NOW YOU WANT TO STEAL THE ONLY BOY I'VE EVER FANCIED.

THAT'S NOT TRUE! HOW CAN YOU BE SO HORRIBLE TO ME WHEN MY PARENTS MIGHT SPLIT UP?